Smith of
Wootton Major

Works by J.R.R. Tolkien

THE HOBBIT
LEAF BY NIGGLE
ON FAIRY-STORIES
FARMER GILES OF HAM
THE HOMECOMING OF BEORHTNOTH
THE LORD OF THE RINGS
THE ADVENTURES OF TOM BOMBADIL
THE ROAD GOES EVER ON (WITH DONALD SWANN)
SMITH OF WOOTTON MAJOR

Works published posthumously

SIR GAWAIN AND THE GREEN KNIGHT, PEARL AND SIR ORFEO*
THE FATHER CHRISTMAS LETTERS
THE SILMARILLION*
PICTURES BY J.R.R. TOLKIEN*
UNFINISHED TALES*
THE LETTERS OF J.R.R. TOLKIEN*
FINN AND HENGEST
MR. BLISS
THE MONSTERS AND THE CRITICS & OTHER ESSAYS*
ROVERANDOM
THE CHILDREN OF HÚRIN*
THE LEGEND OF SIGURD AND GUDRÚN*
THE FALL OF ARTHUR*
BEOWULF: A TRANSLATION AND COMMENTARY*

The History of Middle-earth – by Christopher Tolkien

I THE BOOK OF LOST TALES, PART ONE
II THE BOOK OF LOST TALES, PART TWO
III THE LAYS OF BELERIAND
IV THE SHAPING OF MIDDLE-EARTH
V THE LOST ROAD AND OTHER WRITINGS
VI THE RETURN OF THE SHADOW
VII THE TREASON OF ISENGARD
VIII THE WAR OF THE RING
IX SAURON DEFEATED
X MORGOTH'S RING
XI THE WAR OF THE JEWELS
XII THE PEOPLES OF MIDDLE-EARTH

* Edited by Christopher Tolkien

J.R.R. TOLKIEN

Smith of Wootton Major

EXTENDED EDITION

Edited by Verlyn Flieger

With illustrations by Pauline Baynes

HarperCollins*Publishers*

HarperCollins*Publishers*
1 London Bridge Street, London SE1 9GF
www.tolkien.co.uk

www.tolkienestate.com

Published by HarperCollins*Publishers* 2015

2

Smith of Wootton Major first published in Great Britain
by George Allen & Unwin 1967

Smith of Wootton Major 'Extended edition' first published in Great Britain by
HarperCollins*Publishers* 2005

Copyright © The Tolkien Trust 1967, 2005
Foreword, afterword and notes copyright © HarperCollins*Publishers* 2005
Illustrations copyright © HarperCollins*Publishers* 1967, 1980

® and 'Tolkien'® are registered trade marks of
The Tolkien Estate Limited

The illustrations and typescript and manuscript pages are reproduced courtesy of the
Bodleian Library, University of Oxford, from their holdings labelled: MS. Tolkien 6, fols.
98r, 99, 3r-v, 4r, 13r-v, 32r-v, 37r-v, 38r, 41-44r-v; and 10, fols. 48, 50, 51, 52, 53, 54,
55, 56, 58, 59 (2 images), 60 (detail)

ISBN 978-0-00-755728-8

Set in Plantin Light

Printed and bound in China by RR Donnelley APS

All rights reserved. No part of this publication may be reproduced,
stored in a retrieval system, or transmitted, in any form or by any means,
electronic, mechanical, photocopying, recording or otherwise, without the
prior permission of the publishers.

This book is sold subject to the condition that it shall not, by way of trade
or otherwise, be lent, re-sold, hired out or otherwise circulated without
the publisher's prior consent in any form of binding or cover other than
that in which it is published and without a similar condition including
this condition being imposed on the subsequent purchaser.

MIX
Paper from
responsible sources
FSC® C007454

FSC™ is a non-profit international organisation established to promote
the responsible management of the world's forests. Products carrying the
FSC label are independently certified to assure consumers that they come
from forests that are managed to meet the social, economic and
ecological needs of present and future generations,
and other controlled sources.

Find out more about HarperCollins and the environment at
www.harpercollins.co.uk/green

Note on Orthography and Usage

The transcriptions of Tolkien's notes, comments and drafts are presented as faithfully as possible within the constraints of sense, clarity and consistency. I have corrected obvious typographical errors, but have tried to conform to his spelling, usage, and punctuation, even when, as sometimes was the case, these were inconsistent from instance to instance.

Verlyn Flieger

Contents

Foreword	ix
Smith of Wootton Major	1
Gallery	57
Afterword	67
"Genesis of the story"	85
Tolkien's draft introduction to *The Golden Key*	89
'The Great Cake' Time Scheme and Characters	97
Suggestions for the ending of the story	105
Smith of Wootton Major essay	111
Hybrid draft and transcription of 'The Great Cake'	147
Lake of Tears drafts and transcriptions	175
Notes	179

Foreword

"DON'T READ THIS! Not yet."

It was with this unequivocal admonition that J.R.R. Tolkien began his never-finished introduction to a proposed edition of George MacDonald's *The Golden Key*. The headline words at the top of the page were aimed at a child reader, as the rest of the rather playful introduction (a transcription of which is included in this volume) makes clear. Nevertheless, whether to child reader or adult reader, Tolkien meant what he said.

He had a strong opinion that editorial introductions were an unnecessary intrusion, for they inevitably came between the story and its reader, and affected the first impression of it. In Tolkien's view reader and story should first meet face to face with no intermediary. There should be no one to interpret, or tell the reader what the story was about, or what to think of it. The proper "introduction", Tolkien wrote, should simply be, "Reader, meet *The Golden Key*." So strongly did he feel about this that he left off writing his introduction to MacDonald's story and proceeded instead to write a story of his own, the book you have in your hand, *Smith of Wootton Major*.

SMITH OF WOOTTON MAJOR

There is much to be said about *Smith of Wootton Major*, much of it by Tolkien himself, but it can be postponed in favour of the story. Following Tolkien's instruction, I have placed the introduction to this edition after the story, fitting it in with the end-matter. Don't read it until after you have read and enjoyed the story. Instead:

Reader, meet *Smith of Wootton Major*.

Verlyn Flieger

Smith of Wootton Major

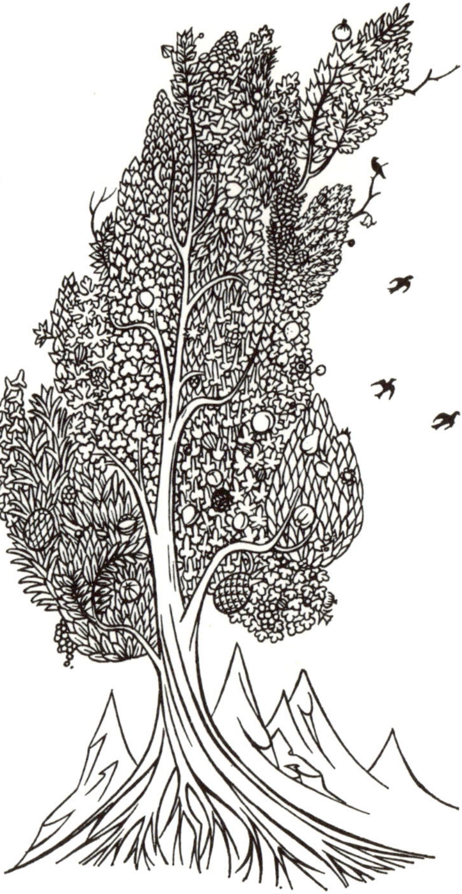

Smith of Wootton Major

THERE was a village once, not very long ago for those with long memories, nor very far away for those with long legs. Wootton Major it was called because it was larger than Wootton Minor, a few miles away deep in the trees; but it was not very large, though it was at that time prosperous, and a fair number of folk lived in it, good, bad, and mixed, as is usual.

It was a remarkable village in its way, being well known in the country round about for the skill of its workers in various crafts, but most of all for its cooking. It had a large Kitchen which belonged to the Village Council, and the Master Cook was an important person. The Cook's House and the Kitchen adjoined the Great Hall, the largest and oldest building in the place and the most beautiful. It was built of good stone and good oak and was well tended, though it was no longer painted or gilded as it had been once upon a time. In the Hall the villagers held their meetings and debates, and their public feasts, and their family gatherings. So the Cook was kept busy, since for all these occasions he had to provide suitable fare. For the festivals, of which there were many in the course of a year, the fare that was thought suitable was plentiful and rich.

There was one festival to which all looked forward, for it was the only one held in winter. It went on for a week, and on its last day at sundown there was a merry-making called The Feast of Good Children, to which not many were invited. No doubt some who deserved to be asked were overlooked, and some who did not were invited by mistake; for that is the way of things, however careful those who arrange such matters may try to be. In any case it was largely by chance of birthday that any child came in for the Twenty-four Feast, since that was only held once in twenty-four years, and only twenty-four children were invited. For that occasion the Master Cook was expected to do his best, and in addition to many other good things it was the custom for him to make the Great Cake. By the excellence (or otherwise) of this his name was chiefly remembered, for a Master Cook seldom if ever lasted long enough in office to make a second Great Cake.

There came a time, however, when the reigning Master Cook, to everyone's surprise, since it had never happened before, suddenly announced that he needed a holiday; and he went away, no one knew where; and when he came back some months later he seemed rather changed. He had been a kind man who liked to see other people enjoying themselves, but he was himself serious, and said very little. Now he was merrier, and often said and did most laughable things; and at feasts he would himself sing gay songs, which was not expected of Master Cooks. Also he brought back with him an Apprentice; and that astonished the Village.

It was not astonishing for the Master Cook to have an apprentice. It was usual. The Master chose one in due time, and he taught him all that he could; and as they both grew older the apprentice took on more of the important work, so that when the Master retired or died there he was, ready to take over the office and become Master Cook in his turn. But this Master had never chosen an apprentice. He had always said 'time enough yet', or 'I'm keeping my eyes open and I'll choose, one when I find one to suit me'. But now he brought with him a mere boy, and not one from the village. He was more lithe than the Wootton lads and quicker, soft-spoken and very polite, but ridiculously young for the work, barely in his teens by the look of him. Still, choosing his apprentice was the Master Cook's affair, and no one had the right to interfere in it; so the boy remained and stayed in the Cook's House until he was old enough to find lodgings for himself. People soon became used to seeing him about, and he made a few friends. They and the Cook called him Alf, but to the rest he was just Prentice.

The next surprise came only three years later. One spring morning the Master Cook took off his tall white hat, folded up his clean aprons, hung up his white coat, took a stout ash stick and a small bag, and departed. He said goodbye to the apprentice. No one else was about.

'Goodbye for now, Alf,' he said. 'I leave you to manage things as best you can, which is always very well. I expect it will turn out all right. If we meet again, I hope to hear all about it. Tell them that I've gone on another holiday, but this time I shan't be coming back again.'

There was quite a stir in the village when Prentice gave this message to people who came to the Kitchen. 'What a thing to do!' they said. 'And without warning or farewell! What are we going to do without any Master Cook? He has left no one to take his place.' In all their discussions no one ever thought of making young Prentice into Cook. He had grown a bit taller but still looked like a boy, and he had only served for three years.

In the end for lack of anyone better they appointed a man of the village, who could cook well enough in a small way. When he was younger he had helped the Master at busy times, but the Master had never taken to him and would not have him as apprentice. He was now a solid sort of man with a wife and children, and careful with money. 'At any rate he won't go off without notice,' they said, 'and poor cooking is better than none. It is seven years till the next Great Cake, and by that time he should be able to manage it.'

Nokes, for that was his name, was very pleased with the turn things had taken. He had always wished to become Master Cook, and had never doubted that he could manage it. For some time, when he was alone in the Kitchen, he used to put on the tall white hat and look at himself in a polished frying pan and say: 'How do you do, Master. That hat suits you properly, might have been made for you. I hope things go well with you.'

Things went well enough; for at first Nokes did his best, and he had Prentice to help him. Indeed he learned a lot from him by watching him slyly, though that Nokes never admitted. But in due course the time for the Twenty-four Feast drew near, and Nokes had to think about making the Great Cake. Secretly he was worried about it, for although with seven years' practice he could turn out passable cakes and pastries for ordinary occasions, he knew that his Great Cake would be eagerly awaited, and would have to satisfy severe critics. Not only the children. A smaller cake of the same materials and baking had to be provided for those who came to help at the feast. Also it was expected that the Great Cake should have something novel and surprising about it and not be a mere repetition of the one before.

His chief notion was that it should be very sweet and rich; and he decided that it should be entirely covered in sugar-icing (at which Prentice had a clever hand). 'That will make it pretty and fairylike,' he thought. Fairies and sweets were two of the very few notions he had about the tastes of children. Fairies he thought one grew out of; but of sweets he remained very fond. 'Ah! fairylike,' he said, 'that gives me an idea'; and so it came into his head that he would stick a little doll on a pinnacle in the middle of the Cake, dressed all in white, with a little wand in her hand ending in a tinsel star, and *Fairy Queen* written in pink icing round her feet.

But when he began preparing the materials for the cake-making he found that he had only dim memories of what should go *inside* a Great Cake; so he looked in some old books of recipes left behind by previous cooks. They puzzled him, even when he could make out their handwriting, for they mentioned many things that he had not heard of, and some that he had forgotten and now had no time to get; but he thought he might try one or two of the spices that the books spoke of. He scratched his head and remembered an old black box with several different compartments in which the last Cook had once kept spices and other things for special cakes. He had not looked at it since he took over, but after a search he found it on a high shelf in the store-room.

He took it down and blew the dust off the lid; but when he opened it he found that very little of the spices was left, and they were dry and musty. But in one compartment in the corner he discovered a small star, hardly as big as one of our sixpences, black-looking as if it was made of silver but was tarnished. 'That's funny!' he said as he held it up to the light.

'No, it isn't!' said a voice behind him, so suddenly that he jumped. It was the voice of Prentice, and he had never spoken to the Master in that tone before. Indeed he seldom spoke to Nokes at all unless he was spoken to first. Very right and proper in a youngster; he might be clever with icing but he had a lot to learn yet: that was Nokes's opinion.

'What do you mean, young fellow?' he said, not much pleased. 'If it isn't funny what is it?'

'It is *fay*,' said Prentice. 'It comes from Faery.'

Then the Cook laughed. 'All right, all right,' he said. 'It means much the same; but call it that if you like. You'll grow up some day. Now you can get on with stoning the raisins. If you notice any funny fairy ones, tell me.'

'What are you going to do with the star, Master?' said Prentice.

'Put it into the Cake, of course,' said the Cook. 'Just the thing, especially if it's *fairy*,' he sniggered. 'I daresay you've been to children's parties yourself, and not so long ago either, where little trinkets like this were stirred into the mixture, and little coins and what not. Anyway we do that in this village: it amuses the children.'

'But this isn't a trinket, Master, it's a fay-star,' said Prentice.

'So you've said already,' snapped the Cook. 'Very well, I'll tell the children. It'll make them laugh.'

'I don't think it will, Master,' said Prentice. 'But it's the right thing to do, quite right.'

SMITH OF WOOTTON MAJOR

'Who do you think you're talking to?' said Nokes.

In time the Cake was made and baked and iced, mostly by Prentice. 'As you are so set on fairies, I'll let you make the Fairy Queen,' Nokes said to him.

'Very good, Master,' he answered. 'I'll do it if you are too busy. But it was your idea and not mine.'

'It's my place to have ideas, and not yours,' said Nokes.

At the Feast the Cake stood in the middle of the long table, inside a ring of twenty-four red candles. Its top rose into a small white mountain, up the sides of which grew little trees glittering as if with frost; on its summit stood a tiny white figure on one foot like a snow-maiden dancing, and in her hand was a minute wand of ice sparkling with light.

The children looked at it with wide eyes, and one or two clapped their hands, crying: 'Isn't it pretty and fairylike!' That delighted the Cook, but the apprentice looked displeased. They were both present: the Master to cut up the Cake when the time came, and the apprentice to sharpen the knife and hand it to him.

At last the Cook took the knife and stepped up to the table. 'I should tell you, my dears,' he said, 'that

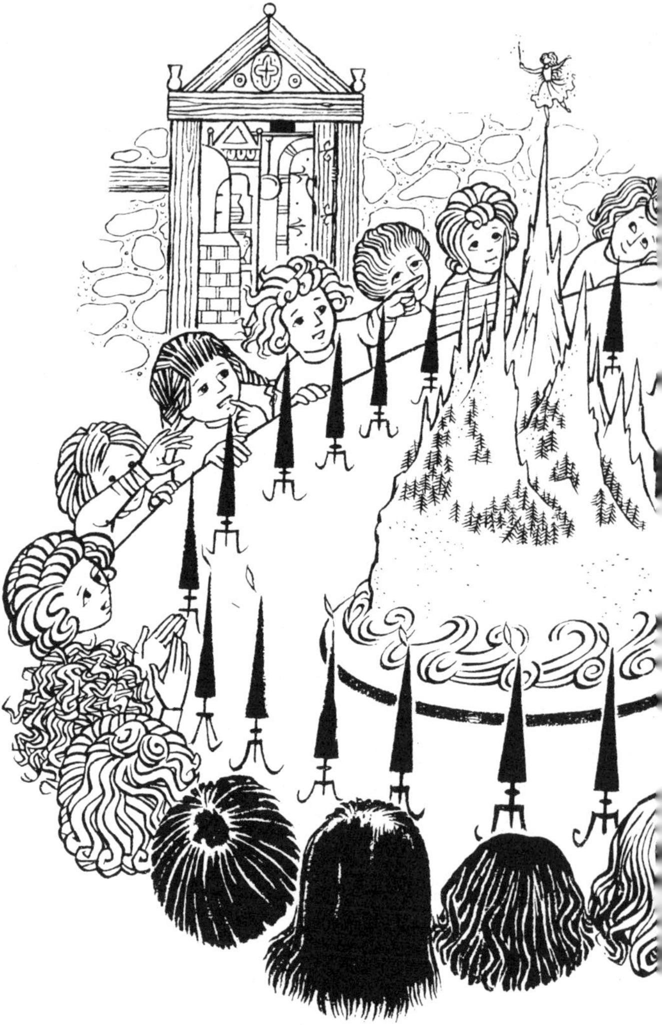

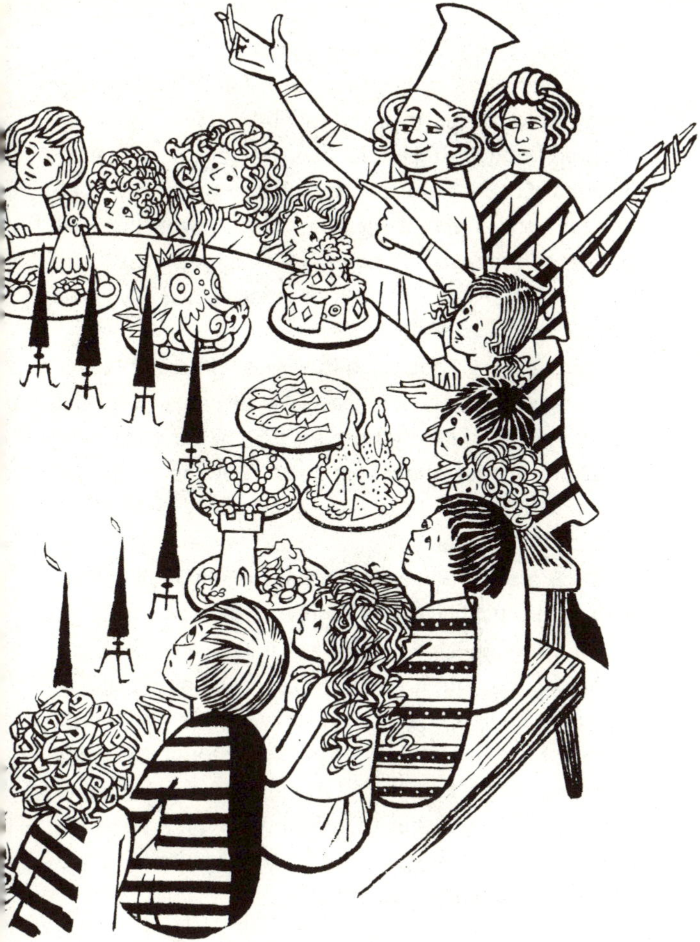

inside this lovely icing there is a cake made of many nice things to eat; but also stirred well in there are many pretty little things, trinkets and little coins and what not, and I'm told that it is lucky to find one in your slice. There are twenty-four in the Cake, so there should be one for each of you, if the Fairy Queen plays fair. But she doesn't always do so: she's a tricky little creature. You ask Mr Prentice.' The apprentice turned away and studied the faces of the children.

'No! I'm forgetting,' said the Cook. 'There's twenty-five this evening. There's also a little silver star, a special magic one, or so Mr Prentice says. So be careful! If you break one of your pretty front teeth on it, the magic star won't mend it. But I expect it's a specially lucky thing to find, all the same.'

It was a good cake, and no one had any fault to find with it, except that it was no bigger than was needed. When it was all cut up there was a large slice for each of the children, but nothing left over: no coming again. The slices soon disappeared, and every now and then a trinket or a coin was discovered. Some found one, and some found two, and several found none; for that is the way luck goes, whether there is a doll with a wand on the cake or not. But when the Cake was all eaten, there was no sign of any magic star.

'Bless me!' said the Cook. 'Then it can't have been made of silver after all; it must have melted. Or perhaps Mr Prentice was right and it was really magical, and it's just vanished and gone back to Fairyland. Not a nice trick to play, I don't think.' He looked at Prentice with a smirk, and Prentice looked at him with dark eyes and did not smile at all.

All the same, the silver star was indeed a fay-star: the apprentice was not one to make mistakes about things of that sort. What had happened was that one of the boys at the Feast had swallowed it without ever noticing it, although he had found a silver coin in his slice and had given it to Nell, the little girl next to him: she looked so disappointed at finding nothing lucky in hers. He sometimes wondered what had really become of the star, and did not know that it had remained with him, tucked away in some place where it could not be felt; for that was what it was intended to do. There it waited for a long time, until its day came.

The Feast had been in mid-winter, but it was now June, and the night was hardly dark at all. The boy got up before dawn, for he did not wish to sleep: it was his tenth birthday. He looked out of the window, and the world seemed quiet and expectant. A little breeze, cool and fragrant, stirred the waking trees. Then the dawn came, and far away he heard the dawn-song of the birds beginning, growing as it came towards him, until it rushed over him, filling all the land round the house, and passed on like a wave of music into the West, as the sun rose above the rim of the world.

'It reminds me of Faery,' he heard himself say; 'but in Faery the people sing too.' Then he began to sing, high and clear, in strange words that he seemed to know by heart; and in that moment the star fell out of his mouth and he caught it on his open hand. It was bright silver now, glistening in the sunlight; but it quivered and rose a little, as if it was about to fly away. Without thinking he clapped his hand to his head, and there the star stayed in the middle of his forehead, and he wore it for many years.

Few people in the village noticed it though it was not invisible to attentive eyes; but it became part of his face, and it did not usually shine at all. Some of its light passed into his eyes; and his voice, which had begun to grow beautiful as soon as the star came to him, became ever more beautiful as he grew up. People liked to hear him speak, even if it was no more than a 'good morning'.

He became well known in his country, not only in his own village but in many others round about, for his good workmanship. His father was a smith, and he followed him in his craft and bettered it. Smithson he was called while his father was still alive, and then just Smith. For by that time he was the best smith between Far Easton and the Westwood, and he could make all kinds of things of iron in his smithy. Most of them, of course, were plain and useful, meant for daily needs: farm tools, carpenters' tools, kitchen tools and pots and pans, bars and bolts and hinges, pot-hooks, fire-dogs, and horse-shoes, and the like. They were strong and lasting, but they also had a grace about them, being shapely in their kinds, good to handle and to look at.

But some things, when he had time, he made for delight; and they were beautiful, for he could work iron into wonderful forms that looked as light and delicate as a spray of leaves and blossom, but kept the stern strength of iron, or seemed even stronger. Few could pass by one of the gates or lattices that he made without stopping to admire it; no one could pass through it once it was shut. He sang when he was making things of this sort; and when Smith began to sing those nearby stopped their own work and came to the smithy to listen.

That was all that most people knew about him. It was enough indeed and more than most men and women in the village achieved, even those who were skilled and hardworking. But there was more to know. For Smith became acquainted with Faery, and some regions of it he knew as well as any mortal can; though since too many had become like Nokes, he spoke of this to few people, except his wife and his children. His wife was Nell, to whom he gave the silver coin, and his daughter was Nan, and his son was Ned Smithson. From them it could not have been kept secret anyway, for they sometimes saw the star shining on his forehead, when he came back from one of the long walks he would take alone now and then in the evening, or when he returned from a journey.

From time to time he would go off, sometimes walking, sometimes riding, and it was generally supposed that it was on business; and sometimes it was, and sometimes it was not. At any rate not to get orders for work, or to buy pig-iron and charcoal and other supplies, though he attended to such things with care and

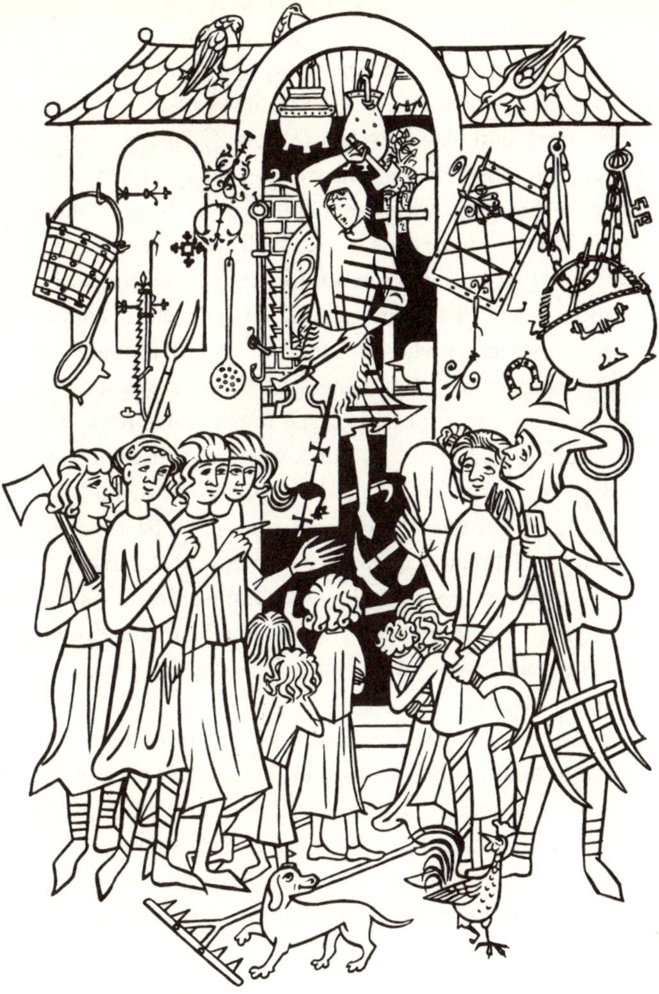

knew how to turn an honest penny into twopence, as the saying went. But he had business of its own kind in Faery, and he was welcome there; for the star shone bright on his brow, and he was as safe as a mortal can be in that perilous country. The Lesser Evils avoided the star, and from the Greater Evils he was guarded.

For that he was grateful, for he soon became wise and understood that the marvels of Faery cannot be approached without danger, and that many of the Evils cannot be challenged without weapons of power too great for any mortal to wield. He remained a learner and explorer, not a warrior; and though in time he could have forged weapons that in his own world would have had power enough to become the matter of great tales and be worth a king's ransom, he knew that in Faery they would have been of small account. So among all the things that he made it is not remembered that he ever forged a sword or a spear or an arrow-head.

In Faery at first he walked for the most part quietly among the lesser folk and the gentler creatures in the woods and meads of fair valleys, and by the bright waters in which at night strange stars shone and at dawn the gleaming peaks of far mountains were mirrored. Some of his briefer visits he spent looking only

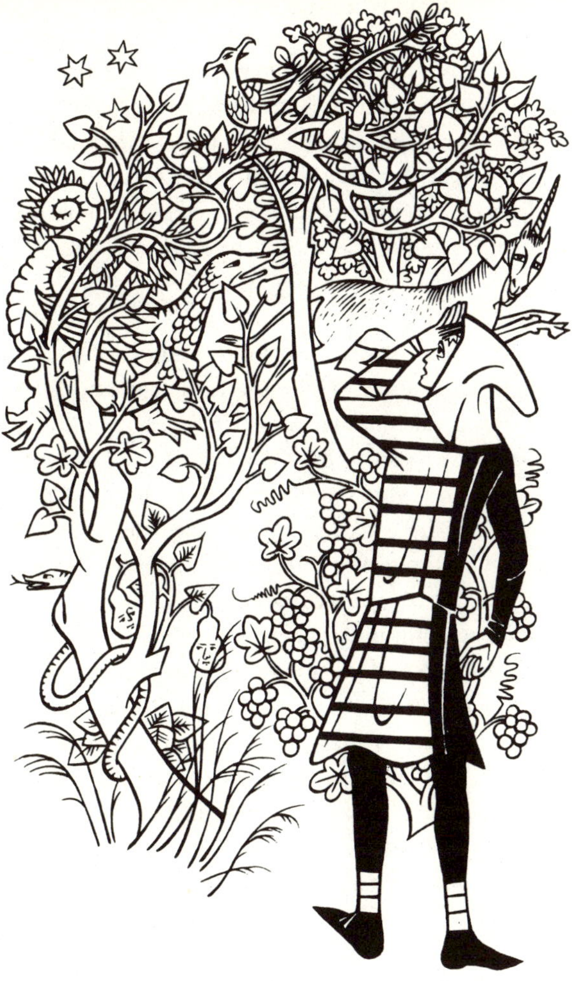

at one tree or one flower; but later in longer journeys he had seen things of both beauty and terror that he could not clearly remember nor report to his friends, though he knew that they dwelt deep in his heart. But some things he did not forget, and they remained in his mind as wonders and mysteries that he often recalled.

✦

When he first began to walk far without a guide he thought he would discover the further bounds of the land; but great mountains rose before him, and going by long ways round about them he came at last to a desolate shore. He stood beside the Sea of Windless Storm where the blue waves like snow-clad hills roll silently out of Unlight to the long strand, bearing the white ships that return from battles on the Dark Marches of which men know nothing. He saw a great ship cast high upon the land, and the waters fell back in foam without a sound. The elven mariners were tall and terrible; their swords shone and their spears glinted and a piercing light was in their eyes. Suddenly they lifted up their voices in a song of triumph, and his heart was shaken with fear, and he fell upon his face, and they passed over him and went away into the echoing hills.

✦

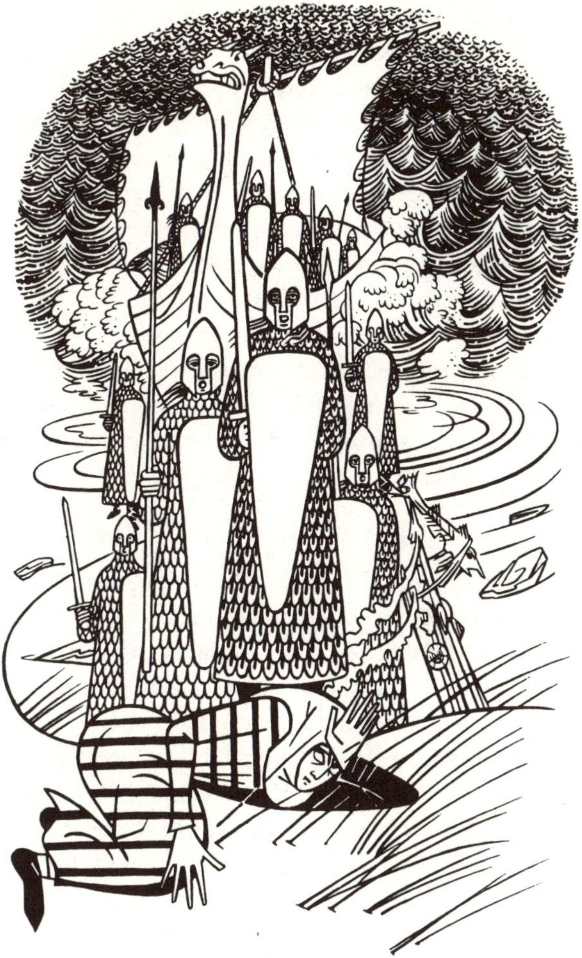

Afterwards he went no more to that strand, believing that he was in an island realm beleaguered by the Sea, and he turned his mind towards the mountains, desiring to come to the heart of the kingdom. Once in these wanderings he was overtaken by a grey mist and strayed long at a loss, until the mist rolled away and he found that he was in a wide plain. Far off there was a great hill of shadow, and out of that shadow, which was its root, he saw the King's Tree springing up, tower upon tower, into the sky, and its light was like the sun at noon; and it bore at once leaves and flowers and fruits uncounted, and not one was the same as any other that grew on the Tree.

He never saw that Tree again, though he often sought for it. On one such journey climbing into the Outer Mountains he came to a deep dale among them, and at its bottom lay a lake, calm and unruffled though a breeze stirred the woods that surrounded it. In that dale the light was like a red sunset, but the light came up from the lake. From a low cliff that overhung it he looked down, and it seemed that he could see to an immeasurable depth; and there he beheld strange shapes of flame bending and branching and wavering like great weeds in a sea-dingle, and fiery creatures went to and fro among them. Filled with wonder he went down to the water's edge and tried it with his foot, but it was not water: it was harder than stone and sleeker than glass. He stepped on it and he fell heavily, and a ringing boom ran across the lake and echoed in its shores.

At once the breeze rose to a wild Wind, roaring like a great beast, and it swept him up and flung him on the shore, and it drove him up the slopes whirling and falling like a dead leaf. He put his arms about the stem of a young birch and clung to it, and the Wind wrestled fiercely with them, trying to tear him away; but the birch was bent down to the ground by the blast and enclosed him in its branches. When at last the Wind passed on he rose and saw that the birch was naked. It was stripped of every leaf, and it wept, and tears fell from its branches like rain. He set his hand upon its white bark, saying: 'Blessed be the birch! What can I do to make amends or give thanks?' He felt the answer of the tree pass up from his hand: 'Nothing,' it said. 'Go away! The Wind is hunting you. You do not belong here. Go away and never return!'

As he climbed back out of that dale he felt the tears of the birch trickle down his face and they were bitter on his lips. His heart was saddened as he went on his long road, and for some time he did not enter Faery again. But he could not forsake it, and when he returned his desire was still stronger to go deep into the land.

✦

At last he found a road through the Outer Mountains, and he went on till he came to the Inner Mountains, and they were high and sheer and daunting. Yet in the end he found a pass that he could scale, and upon a day of days greatly daring he came through a narrow cleft and looked down, though he did not know it, into the Vale of Evermorn where the green surpasses the green of the meads of Outer Faery as they surpass ours in our springtime. There the air is so lucid that eyes can see the red tongues of birds as they sing on the trees upon the far side of the valley, though that is very wide and the birds are no greater than wrens.

On the inner side the mountains went down in long slopes filled with the sound of bubbling waterfalls, and in great delight he hastened on. As he set foot upon the grass of the Vale he heard elven voices singing, and on a lawn beside a river bright with lilies he came upon many maidens dancing. The speed and the grace and the everchanging modes of their movements enchanted him, and he stepped forward towards their ring. Then

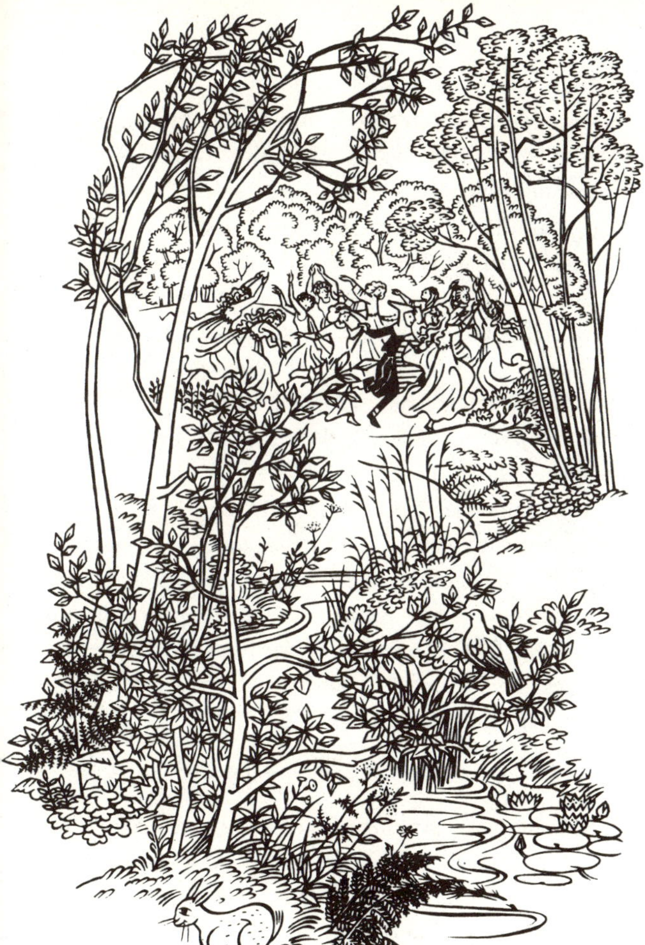

suddenly they stood still, and a young maiden with flowing hair and kilted skirt came out to meet him.

She laughed as she spoke to him, saying: 'You are becoming bold, Starbrow, are you not? Have you no fear what the Queen might say, if she knew of this? Unless you have her leave.' He was abashed, for he became aware of his own thought and knew that she read it: that the star on his forehead was a passport to go wherever he wished; and now he knew that it was not. But she smiled as she spoke again: 'Come! Now that you are here you shall dance with me'; and she took his hand and led him into the ring.

There they danced together, and for a while he knew what it was to have the swiftness and the power and the joy to accompany her. For a while. But soon as it seemed they halted again, and she stooped and took up a white flower from before her feet, and she set it in his hair. 'Farewell now!' she said. 'Maybe we shall meet again, by the Queen's leave.'

He remembered nothing of the journey home from that meeting, until he found himself riding along the roads in his own country; and in some villages people stared at him in wonder and watched him till he rode out of sight. When he came to his own house his daughter ran out and greeted him with delight – he had returned sooner than was expected, but none too soon for those that awaited him. 'Daddy!' she cried. 'Where have you been? Your star is shining bright!'

When he crossed the threshold the star dimmed again; but Nell took him by the hand and led him to the hearth, and there she turned and looked at him. 'Dear Man,' she said, 'where have you been and what have you seen? There is a flower in your hair.' She lifted it gently from his head, and it lay on her hand. It seemed like a thing seen from a great distance, yet there it was, and a light came from it that cast shadows on the walls of the room, now growing dark in the evening. The shadow of the man before her loomed up and its great head was bowed over her. 'You look like a giant, Dad,' said his son, who had not spoken before.

The flower did not wither nor grow dim; and they kept it as a secret and a treasure. The smith made a little casket with a key for it, and there it lay and was handed down for many generations in his kin; and those who inherited the key would at times open the casket and look long at the Living Flower, till the casket closed again: the time of its shutting was not theirs to choose.

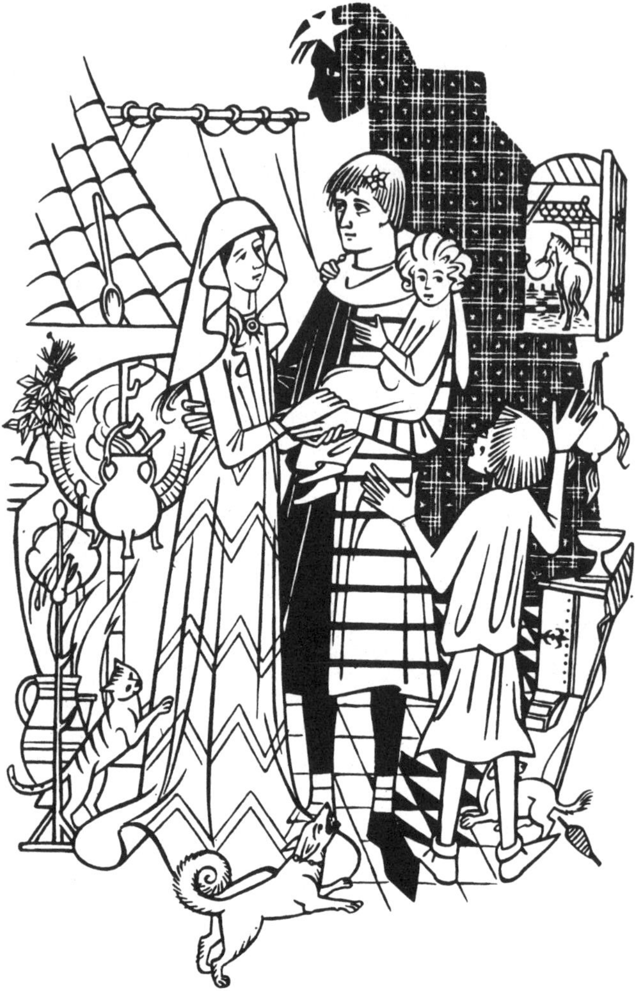

The years did not halt in the village. Many now had passed. At the Children's Feast when he received the star the smith was not yet ten years old. Then came another Twenty-four Feast, by which time Alf had become Master Cook and had chosen a new apprentice, Harper. Twelve years later the smith had returned with the Living Flower; and now another Children's Twenty-four Feast was due in the winter to come. One day in that year Smith was walking in the woods of Outer Faery, and it was autumn. Golden leaves were on the boughs and red leaves were on the ground. Footsteps came behind him, but he did not heed them or turn round, for he was deep in thought.

On that visit he had received a summons and had made a far journey. Longer it seemed to him than any he had yet made. He was guided and guarded, but he had little memory of the ways that he had taken; for often he had been blindfolded by mist or by shadow, until at last he came to a high place under a night-sky of innumerable stars. There he was brought before the Queen herself. She wore no crown and had no throne. She stood there in her majesty and her glory, and all about her was a great host shimmering and glittering like the stars above; but she was taller than the points of their great spears, and upon her head there burned a white flame. She made a sign for him to approach, and trembling he stepped forward. A high clear trumpet sounded, and behold! they were alone.

He stood before her, and he did not kneel in courtesy, for he was dismayed and felt that for one so lowly all gestures were in vain. At length he looked up and beheld her face and her eyes bent gravely upon him; and he was troubled and amazed, for in that moment he knew her again: the fair maid of the Green Vale, the dancer at whose feet the flowers sprang. She smiled seeing his memory, and drew towards him; and they spoke long together, for the most part without words, and he learned many things in her thought, some of which gave him joy, and others filled him with grief. Then his mind turned back retracing his life, until he came to the day of the Children's Feast and the coming of the star, and suddenly he saw again the little dancing figure with its wand, and in shame he lowered his eyes from the Queen's beauty.

But she laughed again as she had laughed in the Vale of Evermorn. 'Do not be grieved for me, Starbrow,' she said. 'Nor too much ashamed of your own folk. Better a little doll, maybe, than no memory of Faery at all. For some the only glimpse. For some the awaking. Ever since that day you have desired in your heart to see me, and I have granted your wish. But I can give you no more. Now at farewell I will make you my messenger. If you meet the King, say to him: *The time has come. Let him choose.*'

'But Lady of Faery,' he stammered, 'where then is the King?' For he had asked this question many times of the people of Faery, and they had all said the same: 'He has not told us.'

And the Queen answered: 'If he has not told you, Starbrow, then I may not. But he makes many journeys and may be met in unlikely places. Now kneel of your courtesy.'

Then he knelt, and she stooped and laid her hand on his head, and a great stillness came upon him; and he seemed to be both in the World and in Faery, and also outside them and surveying them, so that he was at once in bereavement, and in ownership, and in peace. When after a while the stillness passed he raised his head and stood up. The dawn was in the sky and the stars were pale, and the Queen was gone. Far off he heard the echo of a trumpet in the mountains. The high field where he stood was silent and empty: and he knew that his way now led back to bereavement.

That meeting-place was now far behind him, and here he was, walking among the fallen leaves, pondering all that he had seen and learned. The footsteps came nearer. Then suddenly a voice said at his side: 'Are you going my way, Starbrow?'

He started and came out of his thoughts, and he saw a man beside him. He was tall, and he walked lightly and quickly; he was dressed all in dark green and wore a hood that partly overshadowed his face. The smith was puzzled, for only the people of Faery called him 'Starbrow', but he could not remember ever having seen this man there before; and yet he felt uneasily that he should know him. 'What way are you going then?' he said.

'I am going back to your village now,' the man answered, 'and I hope that you are also returning.'

'I am indeed,' said the smith. 'Let us walk together. But now something has come back to my mind. Before I began my homeward journey a Great Lady gave me a message, but we shall soon be passing from Faery, and I do not think that I shall ever return. Will you?'

'Yes, I shall. You may give the message to me.'

'But the message was to the King. Do you know where to find him?'

'I do. What was the message?'

'The Lady only asked me to say to him: *The time has come. Let him choose.*'

'I understand. Trouble yourself no further.'

They went on then side by side in silence save for the rustle of the leaves about their feet; but after a few miles while they were still within the bounds of Faery the man halted. He turned towards the smith and threw back his hood. Then the smith knew him. He was Alf the Prentice, as the smith still called him in his own mind, remembering always the day when as a youth Alf had stood in the Hall, holding the bright knife for the cutting of the Cake, and his eyes had gleamed in the light of the candles. He must be an old man now, for he had been Master Cook for many years; but here standing under the eaves of the Outer Wood he looked like the apprentice of long ago, though more masterly: there was no grey in his hair nor line on his face, and his eyes gleamed as if they reflected a light.

'I should like to speak to you, Smith Smithson, before we go back to your country,' he said. The smith wondered at that, for he himself had often wished to talk to Alf, but had never been able to do so. Alf had always greeted him kindly and had looked at him with

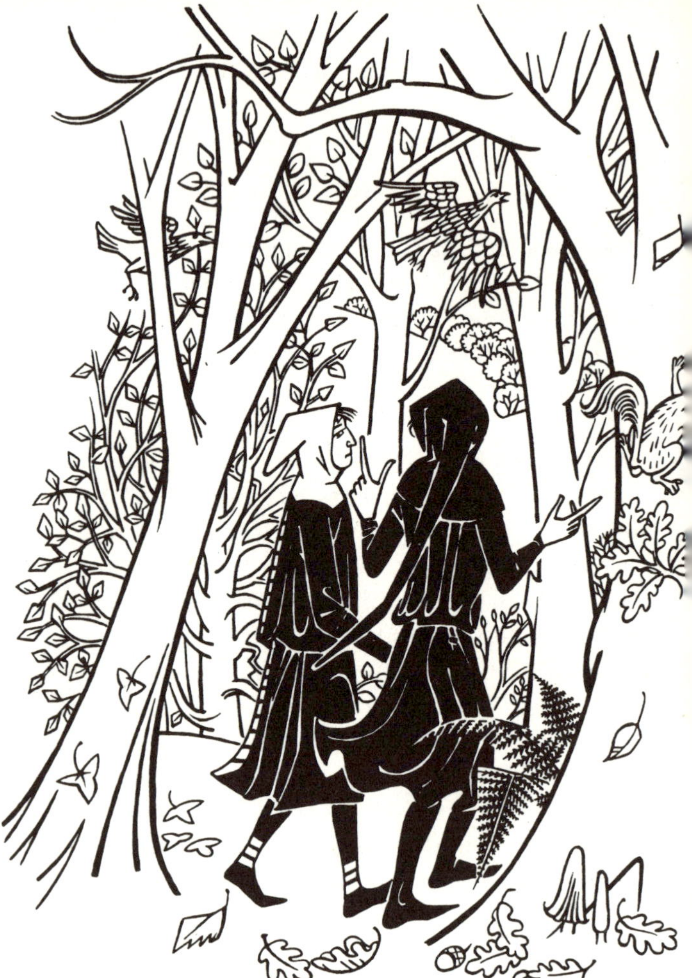

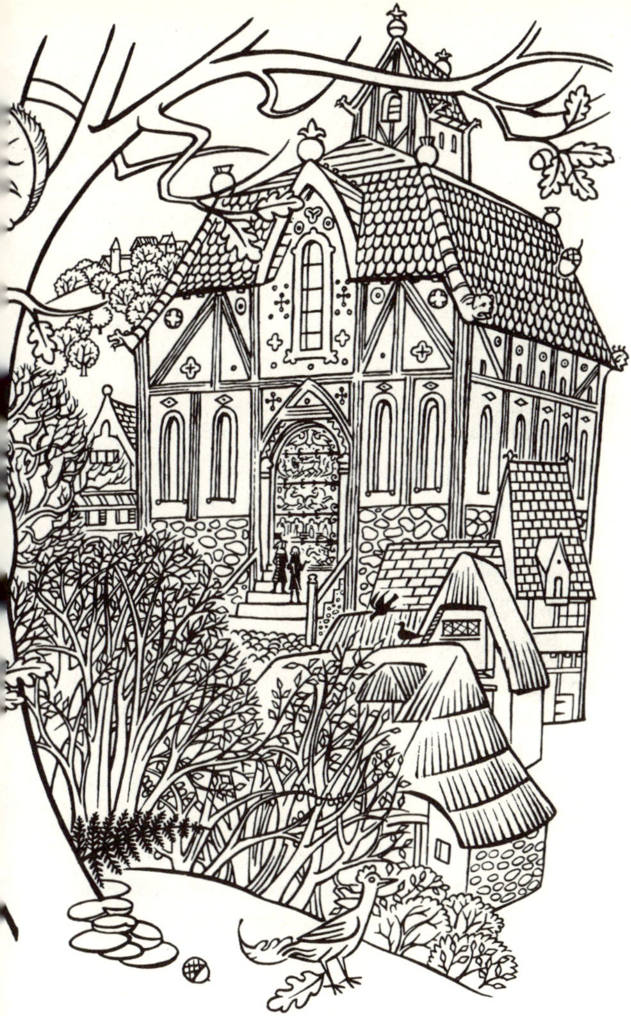

friendly eyes, but had seemed to avoid talking to him alone. He was looking now at the smith with friendly eyes; but he lifted his hand and with his forefinger touched the star on his brow. The gleam left his eyes, and then the smith knew that it had come from the star, and that it must have been shining brightly but now was dimmed. He was surprised and drew away angrily.

'Do you not think, Master Smith,' said Alf, 'that it is time for you to give this thing up?'

'What is that to you, Master Cook?' he answered. 'And why should I do so? Isn't it mine? It came to me, and may a man not keep things that come to him so, at the least as a remembrance?'

'Some things. Those that are free gifts and given for remembrance. But others are not so given. They cannot belong to a man for ever, nor be treasured as heirlooms. They are lent. You have not thought, perhaps, that someone else may need this thing. But it is so. Time is pressing.'

Then the smith was troubled, for he was a generous man, and he remembered with gratitude all that the star had brought to him. 'Then what should I do?' he asked. 'Should I give it to one of the Great in Faery? Should I give it to the King?' And as he said this a hope sprang

SMITH OF WOOTTON MAJOR

in his heart that on such an errand he might once more enter Faery.

'You could give it to me,' said Alf, 'but you might find that too hard. Will you come with me to my storeroom and put it back in the box where your grandfather laid it?'

'I did not know that,' said the smith.

'No one knew but me. I was the only one with him.'

'Then I suppose that you know how he came by the star, and why he put it in the box?'

'He brought it from Faery: that you know without asking,' Alf answered. 'He left it behind in the hope that it might come to you, his only grandchild. So he told me, for he thought that I could arrange that. He was your mother's father. I do not know whether she told you much about him, if indeed she knew much to tell. Rider was his name, and he was a great traveller: he had seen many things and could do many things before he settled down and became Master Cook. But he went away when you were only two years old – and they could find no one better to follow him than Nokes, poor man. Still, as we expected, I became Master in time. This year I shall make another Great Cake: the only Cook, as far as is remembered, ever to make a second one. I wish to put the star in it.'

'Very well, you shall have it,' said the smith. He looked at Alf as if he was trying to read his thought. 'Do you know who will find it?'

'What is that to you, Master Smith?'

'I should like to know, if you do, Master Cook. It might make it easier for me to part with a thing so dear to me. My daughter's child is too young.'

'It might and it might not. We shall see,' said Alf.

They said no more, and they went on their way until they passed out of Faery and came back at last to the village. Then they walked to the Hall; and in the world the sun was now setting and a red light was in the windows. The gilded carvings on the great door glowed, and strange faces of many colours looked down from the waterspouts under the roof. Not long ago the Hall had been re-glazed and re-painted, and there had been much debate on the Council about it. Some disliked it and called it 'new-fangled', but some with more knowledge knew that it was a return to old custom. Still, since it had cost no one a penny and the Master Cook must have paid for it himself, he was allowed to have his own way. But the smith had not seen it in such a light before, and he stood and looked at the Hall in wonder, forgetting his errand.

SMITH OF WOOTTON MAJOR

He felt a touch on his arm, and Alf led him round to a small door at the back. He opened it and led the smith down a dark passage into the store-room. There he lit a tall candle, and unlocking a cupboard he took down from a shelf the black box. It was polished now and adorned with silver scrolls.

He raised the lid and showed it to the smith. One small compartment was empty; the others were now filled with spices, fresh and pungent, and the smith's eyes began to water. He put his hand to his forehead, and the star came away readily, but he felt a sudden stab of pain, and tears ran down his face. Though the star shone brightly again as it lay in his hand, he could not see it, except as a blurred dazzle of light that seemed far away.

'I cannot see clearly,' he said. 'You must put it in for me.' He held out his hand, and Alf took the star and laid it in its place, and it went dark.

The smith turned away without another word and groped his way to the door. On the threshold he found that his sight had cleared again. It was evening and the Even-star was shining in a luminous sky close to the Moon. As he stood for a moment looking at their beauty, he felt a hand on his shoulder and turned.

'You gave me the star freely,' said Alf. 'If you still wish to know to which child it will go, I will tell you.'

'I do indeed.'

'It shall go to any one that you appoint.'

The smith was taken aback and did not answer at once. 'Well,' he said hesitating, 'I wonder what you may think of my choice. I believe you have little reason to love the name of Nokes, but, well, his little great-grandson, Nokes of Townsend's Tim, is coming to the Feast. Nokes of Townsend is quite different.'

'I have observed that,' said Alf. 'He had a wise mother.'

'Yes, my Nell's sister. But apart from the kinship I love little Tim. Though he's not an obvious choice.'

Alf smiled. 'Neither were you,' he said. 'But I agree. Indeed I had already chosen Tim.'

'Then why did you ask me to choose?'

'The Queen wished me to do so. If you had chosen differently I should have given way.'

The smith looked long at Alf. Then suddenly he bowed low. 'I understand at last, sir,' he said. 'You have done us too much honour.'

'I have been repaid,' said Alf. 'Go home now in peace!'

※

When the smith reached his own house on the western outskirts of the village he found his son by the door of the forge. He had just locked it, for the day's work was done, and now he stood looking up the white road by which his father used to return from his journeys. Hearing footsteps, he turned in surprise to see him coming from the village, and he ran forward to meet him. He put his arms about him in loving welcome.

'I've been hoping for you since yesterday, Dad,' he said. Then looking into his father's face he said anxiously: 'How tired you look! You have walked far, maybe?'

'Very far indeed, my son. All the way from Daybreak to Evening.'

They went into the house together, and it was dark except for the fire flickering on the hearth. His son lit candles, and for a while they sat by the fire without speaking; for a great weariness and bereavement was on the smith. At last he looked round, as if coming to himself, and he said: 'Why are we alone?'

His son looked hard at him. 'Why? Mother's over at Minor, at Nan's. It's the little lad's second birthday. They hoped you would be there too.'

'Ah yes. I ought to have been. I should have been,

Ned, but I was delayed; and I have had matters to think of that put all else out of mind for a time. But I did not forget Tomling.'

He put his hand in his breast and drew out a little wallet of soft leather. 'I have brought him something. A trinket old Nokes maybe would call it – but it comes out of Faery, Ned.' Out of the wallet he took a little thing of silver. It was like the smooth stem of a tiny lily from the top of which came three delicate flowers, bending down like shapely bells. And bells they were, for when he shook them gently each flower rang with a small clear note. At the sweet sound the candles flickered and then for a moment shone with a white light.

Ned's eyes were wide with wonder. 'May I look at it, Dad?' he said. He took it with careful fingers and peered into the flowers. 'The work is a marvel!' he said. 'And, Dad, there is a scent in the bells: a scent that reminds me of, reminds me, well, of something I've forgotten.'

'Yes, the scent comes for a little while after the bells have rung. But don't fear to handle it, Ned. It was made for a babe to play with. He can do it no harm, and he'll take none from it.'

The smith put the gift back in the wallet and stowed it away. 'I'll take it over to Wootton Minor myself tomorrow,' he said. 'Nan and her Tom, and Mother, will forgive me, maybe. As for Tomling, his time has not yet come for the counting of days . . . and of weeks, and of months, and of years.'

'That's right. You go, Dad. I'd be glad to go with you; but it will be some time before I can get over to Minor. I couldn't have gone today, even if I hadn't waited here for you. There's a lot of work in hand, and more coming in.'

'No, no, Smith's son! Make it a holiday! The name of grandfather hasn't weakened my arms yet a while. Let the work come! There'll be two pairs of hands to tackle it now, all working days. I shall not be going on journeys again, Ned: not on long ones, if you understand me.'

'It's that way is it, Dad? I wondered what had become of the star. That's hard.' He took his father's hand. 'I'm grieved for you; but there's good in it too, for this house. Do you know, Master Smith, there is much you can teach me yet, if you have the time. And I do not mean only the working of iron.'

They had supper together, and long after they had finished they still sat at the table, while the smith told his son of his last journey in Faery, and of other things that came to his mind – but about the choice of the next holder of the star he said nothing.

At last his son looked at him, and 'Father,' he said, 'do you remember the day when you came back with the Flower? And I said that you looked like a giant by your shadow. The shadow was the truth. So it was the Queen herself that you danced with. Yet you have given up the star. I hope it may go to someone as worthy. The child should be grateful.'

'The child won't know,' said the smith. 'That's the way with such gifts. Well, there it is. I have handed it on and come back to hammer and tongs.'

It is a strange thing, but old Nokes, who had scoffed at his apprentice, had never been able to put out of his mind the disappearance of the star in the Cake, although that event had happened so many years ago. He had grown fat and lazy, and retired from his office when he was sixty (no great age in the village). He was now near the end of his eighties, and was of enormous bulk, for he still ate heavily and doted on sugar. Most of his days, when not at table, he spent in a big chair by the window of his cottage, or by the door if it was fine weather. He liked talking, since he still had many opinions to air; but lately his talk mostly turned to the one Great Cake that he had made (as he was now firmly convinced), for whenever he fell asleep it came into his dreams. Prentice sometimes stopped for a word or two. So the old cook still called him, and he expected himself to be called Master. That Prentice was careful to do; which was a point in his favour, though there were others that Nokes was more fond of.

One afternoon Nokes was nodding in his chair by the door after his dinner. He woke with a start to find Prentice standing by and looking down at him. 'Hullo!' he said. 'I'm glad to see you, for that cake's been on my mind again. I was thinking of it just now in fact. It was the best cake I ever made, and that's saying something. But perhaps you have forgotten it.'

'No, Master. I remember it very well. But what is troubling you? It was a good cake, and it was enjoyed and praised.'

'Of course. I made it. But that doesn't trouble me. It's the little trinket, the star. I cannot make up my mind what became of it. Of course it wouldn't melt. I only said that to stop the children from being frightened. I have wondered if one of them did not swallow it. But is that likely? You might swallow one of those little coins and not notice it, but not that star. It was small but it had sharp points.'

'Yes, Master. But do you really know what the star was made of? Don't trouble your mind about it. Someone swallowed it, I assure you.'

'Then who? Well, I've a long memory, and that day sticks in it somehow. I can recall all the children's names. Let me think. It must have been Miller's Molly! She was greedy and bolted her food. She's as fat as a sack now.'

'Yes, there are some folk who get like that, Master. But Molly did not bolt her cake. She found two trinkets in her slice.'

'Oh, did she? Well, it was Cooper's Harry then. A barrel of a boy with a big mouth like a frog's.'

'I should have said, Master, that he was a nice boy with a large friendly grin. Anyway he was so careful that he took his slice to pieces before he ate it. He found nothing but cake.'

'Then it must have been that little pale girl, Draper's Lily. She used to swallow pins as a baby and came to no harm.'

'Not Lily, Master. She only ate the paste and the sugar, and gave the inside to the boy that sat next to her.'

'Then I give up. Who was it? You seem to have been watching very closely. If you're not making it all up.'

'It was the Smith's son, Master; and I think it was good for him.'

'Go on!' laughed old Nokes. 'I ought to have known you were having a game with me. Don't be ridiculous! Smith was a quiet slow boy then. He makes more noise now: a bit of a songster, I hear; but he's cautious. No risks for him. Chews twice before he swallows, and always did, if you take my meaning.'

'I do, Master. Well, if you won't believe it was Smith, I can't help you. Perhaps it doesn't matter much now. Will it ease your mind if I tell you that the star is back in the box now? Here it is!'

Prentice was wearing a dark green cloak, which Nokes now noticed for the first time. From its folds he produced the black box and opened it under the old cook's nose.

'There is the star, Master, down in the corner.'

Old Nokes began coughing and sneezing, but at last he looked into the box. 'So it is!' he said. 'At least it looks like it.'

'It is the same one, Master. I put it there myself a few days ago. It will go back in the Great Cake this winter.'

'A-ha!' said Nokes, leering at Prentice; and then he laughed till he shook like a jelly. 'I see, I see! Twenty-four children and twenty-four lucky bits, and the star was one extra. So you nipped it out before the baking and kept it for another time. You were always a tricky fellow: nimble one might say. And thrifty: wouldn't waste a bee's knee of butter. Ha, ha, ha! So that was the way of it. I might have guessed. Well, that's cleared up. Now I can have a nap in peace.' He settled down in his chair. 'Mind that prenticeman of yours plays you no tricks! The artful don't know all the arts, they say.' He closed his eyes.

'Goodbye, Master!' said Prentice, shutting the box with such a snap that the cook opened his eyes again. 'Nokes,' he said, 'your knowledge is so great that I have only twice ventured to tell you anything. I told you that the star came from Faery; and I have told you that it went to the smith. You laughed at me. Now at parting I will tell you one thing more. Don't laugh again! You are a vain old fraud, fat, idle and sly. I did most of your work. Without thanks you learned all that you could from me – except respect for Faery, and a little courtesy. You have not even enough to bid me good day.'

'If it comes to courtesy,' said Nokes, 'I see none in calling your elders and betters by ill names. Take your Fairy and your nonsense somewhere else! Good day to you, if that's what you're waiting for. Now go along with you!' He flapped his hand mockingly. 'If you've got one of your fairy friends hidden in the Kitchen, send him to me and I'll have a look at him. If he waves his little wand and makes me thin again, I'll think better of him,' he laughed.

'Would you spare a few moments for the King of Faery?' the other answered. To Nokes's dismay he grew taller as he spoke. He threw back his cloak. He was dressed like a Master Cook at a Feast, but his white garments shimmered and glinted, and on his forehead was a great jewel like a radiant star. His face was young but stern.

'Old man,' he said, 'you are at least not my elder. As to my better: you have often sneered at me behind my back. Do you challenge me now openly?' He stepped forward, and Nokes shrank from him, trembling. He tried to shout for help but found that he could hardly whisper.

'No, sir!' he croaked. 'Don't do me a harm! I'm only a poor old man.'

The King's face softened. 'Alas, yes! You speak the truth. Do not be afraid! Be at ease! But will you not expect the King of Faery to do something for you before he leaves you? I grant you your wish. Farewell! Now go to sleep!'

He wrapped his cloak about him again and went away towards the Hall; but before he was out of sight the old cook's goggling eyes had shut and he was snoring.

When the old cook woke again the sun was going down. He rubbed his eyes and shivered a little, for the autumn air was chilly. 'Ugh! What a dream!' he said. 'It must have been that pork at dinner.'

From that day he became so afraid of having more bad dreams of that sort that he hardly dared eat anything for fear that it might upset him, and his meals became very short and plain. He soon became lean, and his clothes and his skin hung on him in folds and creases. The children called him old Rag-and-Bones. Then for a time he found that he could get about the village again and walk with no more help than a stick; and he lived many years longer than he would otherwise have done. Indeed it is said that he just made his century: the only memorable thing he ever achieved. But till his last year he could be heard saying to any that would listen to his tale: 'Alarming, you might call it; but a silly dream, when you come to think of it. King o' Fairy! Why, he hadn't no wand. And if you stop eating you grow thinner. That's natural. Stands to reason. There ain't no magic in it.'

⋆

The time for the Twenty-four Feast came round. Smith was there to sing songs and his wife to help with the children. Smith looked at them as they sang and danced, and he thought that they were more beautiful and lively than they had been in his boyhood – for a moment it crossed his mind to wonder what Alf might have been doing in his spare time. Any one of them seemed fit to find the star. But his eyes were mostly on Tim: a rather plump little boy, clumsy in the dances, but with a sweet voice in the singing. At table he sat silent watching the sharpening of the knife and the cutting of the Cake. Suddenly, he piped up: 'Dear Mr Cook, only cut me a small slice please. I've eaten so much already, I feel rather full.'

'All right, Tim,' said Alf. 'I'll cut you a special slice. I think you'll find it go down easily.'

Smith watched as Tim ate his cake slowly, but with evident pleasure; though when he found no trinket or coin in it he looked disappointed. But soon a light began to shine in his eyes, and he laughed and became merry, and sang softly to himself. Then he got up and began to dance all alone with an odd grace that he had never shown before. The children all laughed and clapped.

'All is well then,' thought Smith. 'So you are my heir. I wonder what strange places the star will lead you to? Poor old Nokes. Still I suppose he will never know what a shocking thing has happened in his family.'

He never did. But one thing happened at that Feast that pleased him mightily. Before it was over the Master Cook took leave of the children and of all the others that were present.

'I will say goodbye now,' he said. 'In a day or two I shall be going away. Master Harper is quite ready to take over. He is a very good cook, and as you know he comes from your own village. I shall go back home. I do not think you will miss me.'

The children said goodbye cheerfully, and thanked the Cook prettily for his beautiful Cake. Only little Tim took his hand and said quietly, 'I'm sorry.'

In the village there were in fact several families that did miss Alf for some time. A few of his friends, especially Smith and Harper, grieved at his going, and they kept the Hall gilded and painted in memory of Alf. Most people, however, were content. They had had him for a very long time and were not sorry to have a change. But old Nokes thumped his stick on the floor and said roundly: 'He's gone at last! And I'm glad for one. I never liked him. He was artful. Too nimble, you might say.'

Gallery

Having originally published *Smith of Wootton Major* in hardback in 1967, and reissued it in 1975 in paperback (with the two shorter works *Leaf by Niggle* and *The Homecoming of Beorhtnoth Beorhthelm's Son*), publishers George Allen and Unwin released the story for a third time in 1980 in a new anthology entitled *Poems and Stories*. For this new edition, *Smith of Wootton Major*'s illustrator, Pauline Baynes, re-drew her original full-page pen and ink drawings, enhancing them with extra detail, reformatting the two double-page drawings into single pages, and in the case of the elven mariners reworking the composition completely. The original drawings appear alongside the story, and the redrawn versions are presented here.

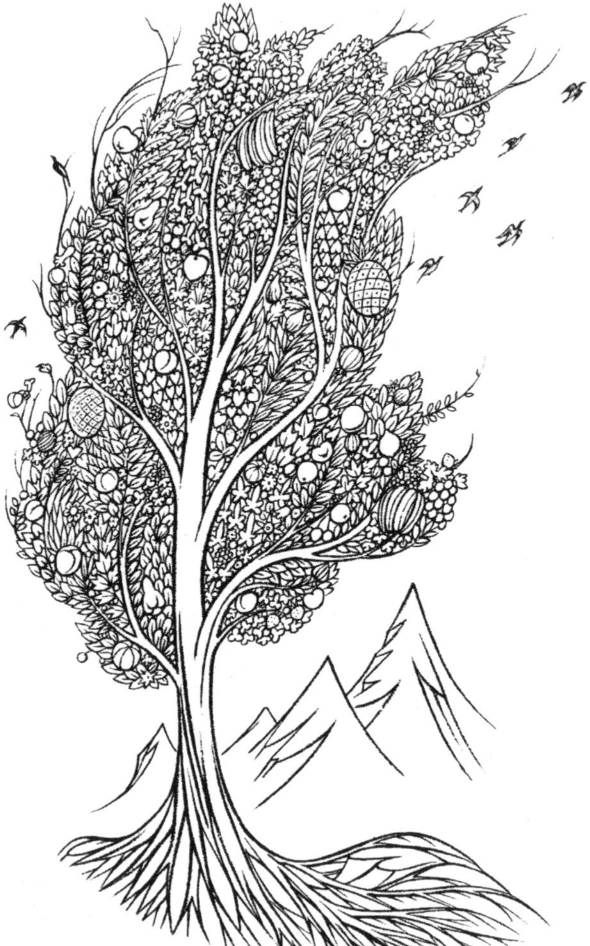

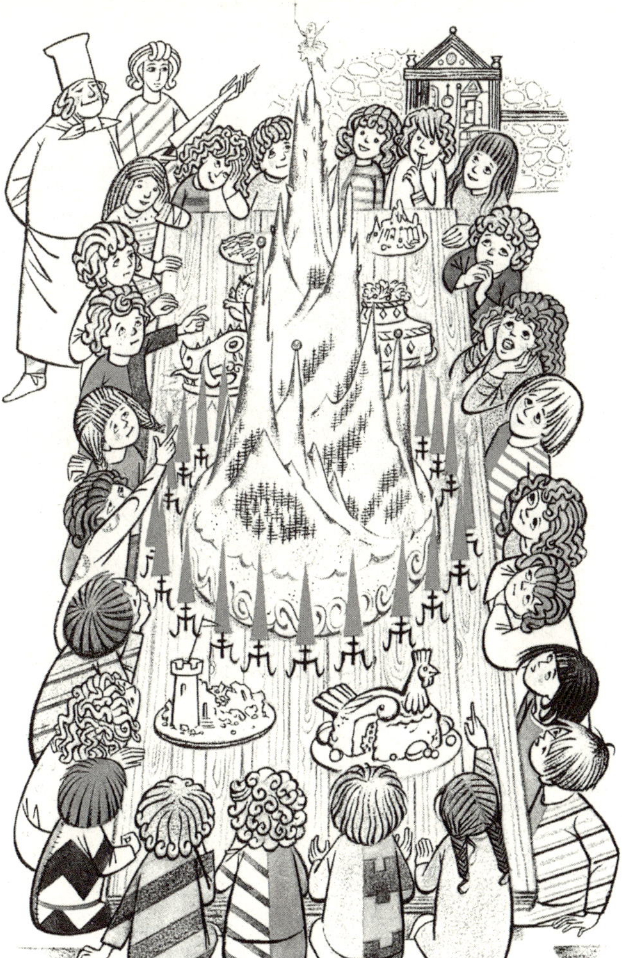

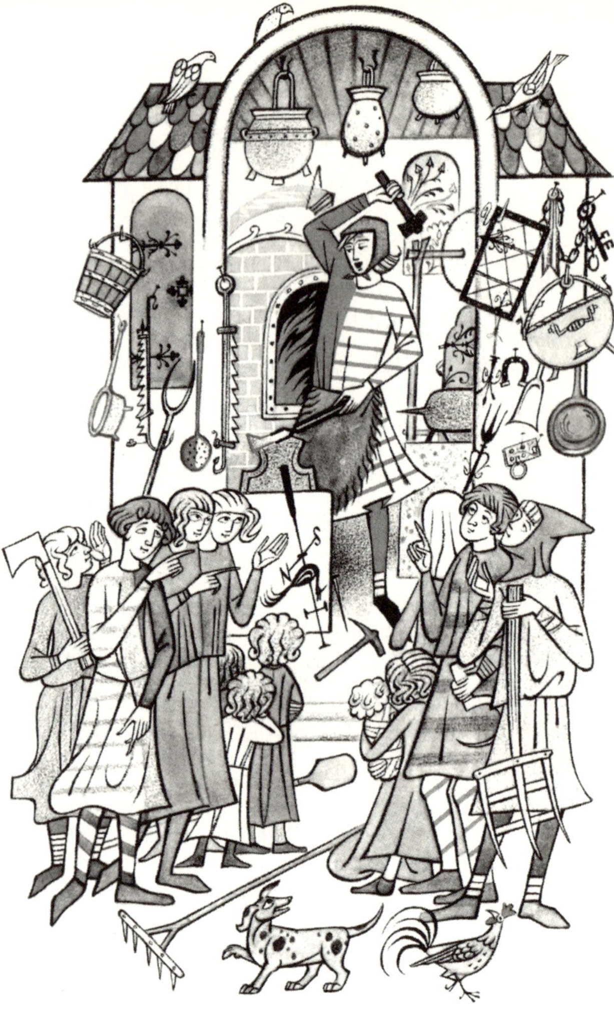

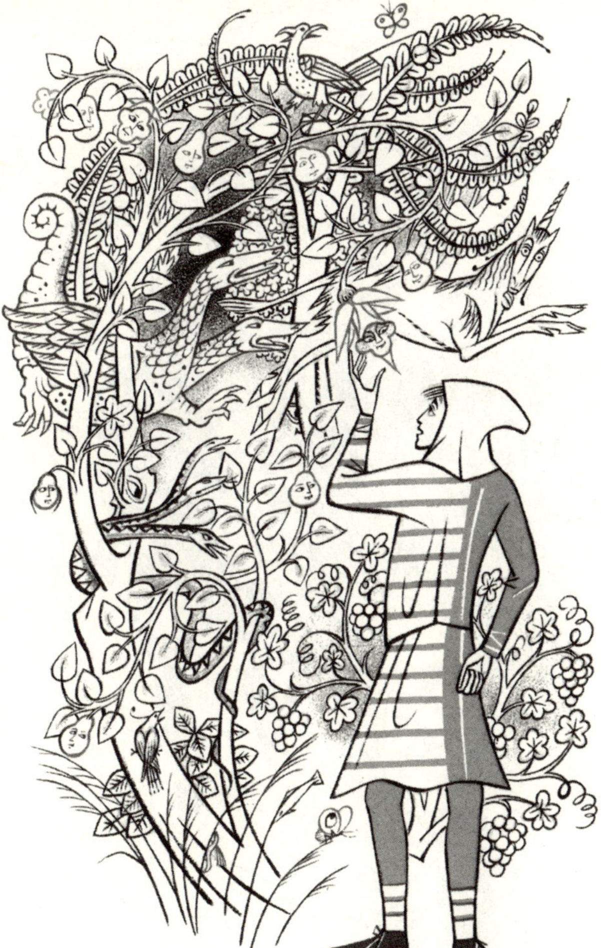

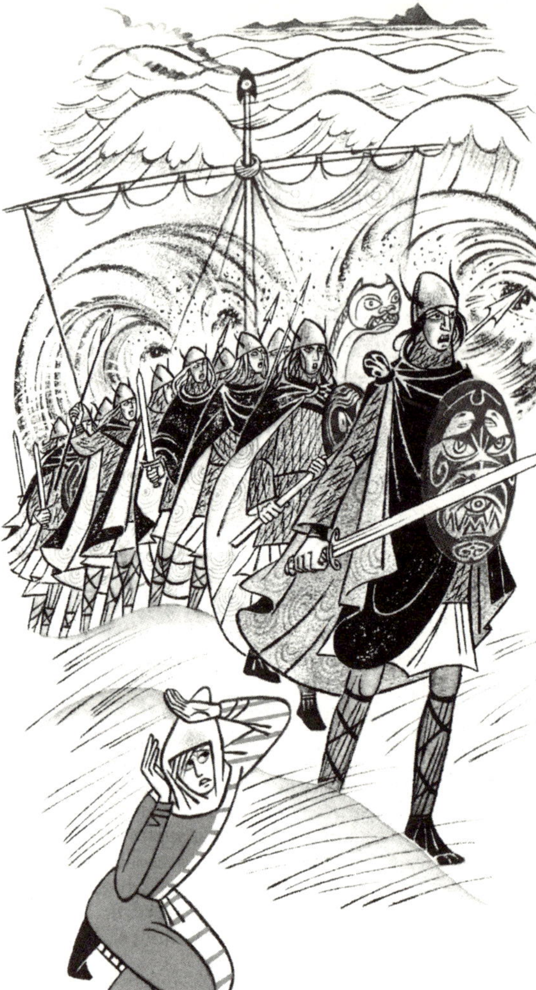

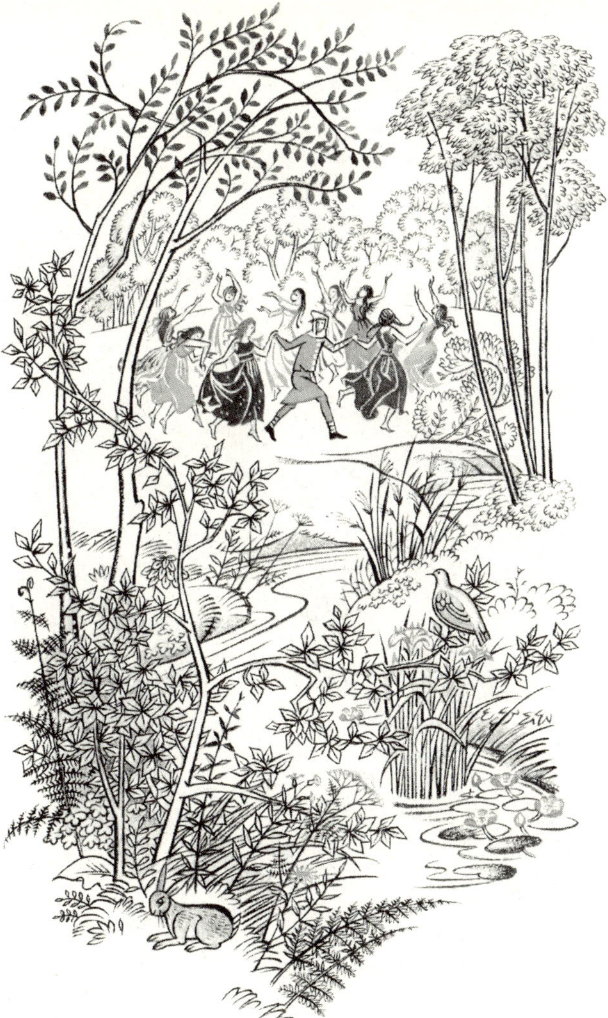

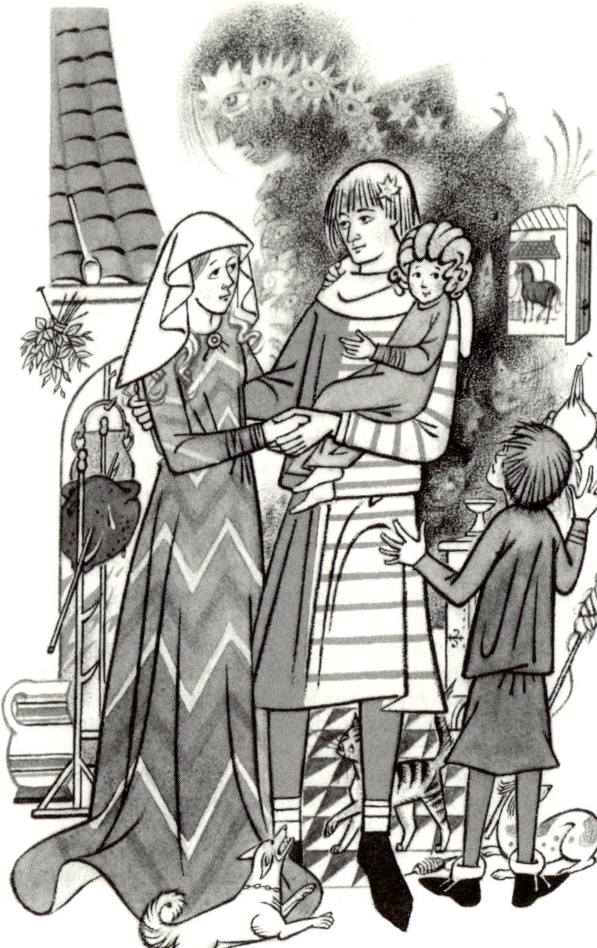

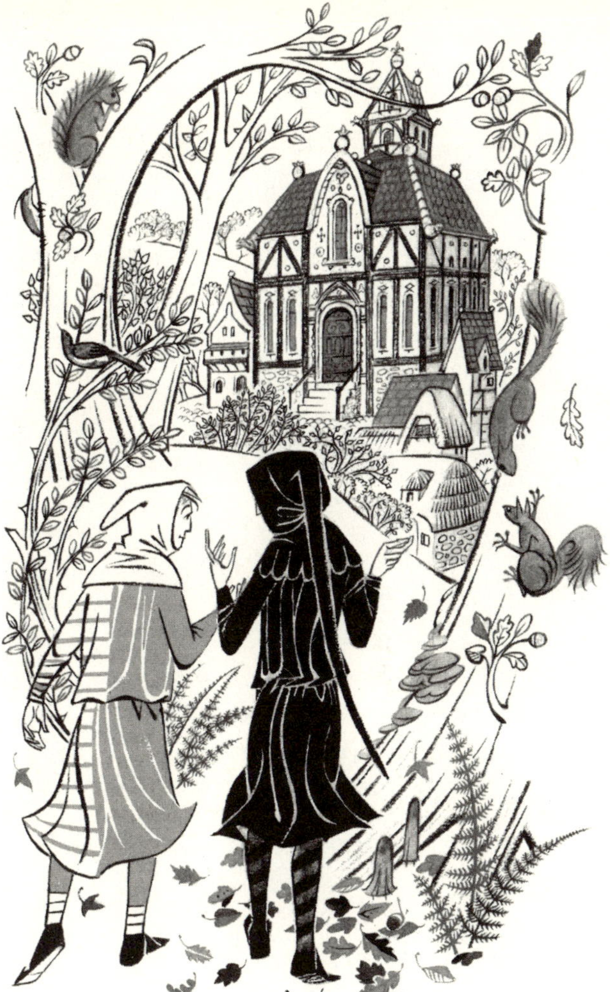

Afterword

The facsimile page at the back of this book comes from the earliest draft version of the story. Typed in black ink, it is overwritten with two distinguishable layers of revision, one written in blue ink with a fountain pen, the other written in red ink with a ballpoint pen. Judging from the appearance, the red layer is the latest, for in places it seems to be written over the blue layer. Reading through the layers, we can reconstruct the author's process from the first creative rush of inspiration through successive stages of modification and elaboration. The page can thus stand as the part for the whole, showing the growth of Tolkien's idea from the initial concept of the village cook and his cake through the development of character and situation to the final story.

Smith of Wootton Major was the last story J.R.R. Tolkien wrote, and was also the last of his work to be published in his lifetime. Composed many years after his other short fictions – *Roverandom*, *Farmer Giles of*

Ham, and *Mr. Bliss* were written in the twenties and thirties, *Leaf by Niggle* in 1943 – *Smith* was begun in 1964, when his great work, *The Lord of the Rings*, was over a decade behind him and his lifelong occupation with the Silmarillion mythology was winding down. Tolkien was 72 when he began the story and 75 when it was published in 1967. The book was thus the product of ripened experience and reflection rather than the exuberant, energetic imagination of his youth and middle years. It has not the adventurous playfulness of *Roverandom*, the robust ironic humour of *Farmer Giles*, the madcap energy of *Mr. Bliss*, nor the transcendent vision and sublime happy ending of *Leaf by Niggle*.

The tale of the craftsman, the smith who journeys into the Otherworld, is Tolkien's homage to the world of imagination he called Faërie – or Fairy or Fayery or Faery; his spellings varied but his concept remained consistent. *Smith* is, as well, his latest, purest, and most uncompromising presentation of that world, and of its effect on a human being who travels there. The story is thus the imaginal realization of the theoretical concept he put forward in his 1939 lecture-essay "On Fairy-Stories". Here, Tolkien was at pains to point out the obvious but often overlooked fact that fairy tales are not about fairies, but about "the *aventures* of men in the Perilous Realm or upon its shadowy marches".

He defended fairies against the popular misconception that they are dainty and diminutive. He defended fairyland against the equally mistaken notion that it is delicate, pretty, and trivial when measured against human affairs. Asserting precisely the opposite, he declared that Faërie "is a perilous land, and in it are pitfalls for the unwary and dungeons for the overbold". "In that realm" he went on, "a man may, perhaps, count himself fortunate to have wandered, but its very richness and strangeness tie the tongue of a traveller who would report them. And while he is there it is dangerous for him to ask too many questions, lest the gates should be shut and the keys be lost." The repeated use of the word "perilous" is the marker of how seriously Tolkien took the concept.

Smith of Wootton Major invites its readers to experience what the fairy-story essay explains, the adventures of a human being in fairyland, as well as the dangers and wonders inherent in that realm. Although the unwary and occasionally overbold Smith encounters both perils and pitfalls, he nevertheless counts himself fortunate to have wandered in Faery (the spelling used in the story). Its "richness and strangeness" do not completely tie his tongue, for he reports his adventures to his own family. Nevertheless, to the other folk of his everyday world, typified by the crass and insensitive Nokes, Smith's (and Tolkien's) Faery is at best a mere children's fable and at worst a joke. Though while he is there Smith asks few questions, still at last the gates are shut against him, and the key, though not lost, must still be given back to be handed on to someone else.

Protected by the star which is his passport, Smith can wander in the enchanted realm, but he remains a visitor, not an inhabitant. No sight or event he encounters is explained to him; no secret is uncovered, no mystery revealed. Faery makes no concession to human curiosity and no allowances for human frailty. Smith puts himself in danger through innocent mistakes, such as setting foot on the hard surface of the lake, which wakens the Wild Wind and gives rise to the birch tree's injunction to go away and never return. In contrast, he also finds friends where he least expects them, as among the dancing maidens, where he partners the Queen of Faery but does not know who she is. The wonderful and beautiful and terrible things he witnesses have a Faerian history and significance of which he remains ignorant. His adventures as a stranger in this strange land parallel those of Tolkien's readers, for whom there is no explanation of what Smith (or they) sees in Faery. We may conjecture that Tolkien wanted his readers to share not just Smith's, but his own experience of wonder and mystery and terror, and perhaps even bewilderment at the richness and strangeness that he found in his own imaginative journeys into Faery.

The story had a curious genesis, developing out of a request from a publisher that Tolkien provide an introduction to a new edition of George MacDonald's fairy story *The Golden Key*. Tolkien began an introduction, attempting to explain the true meaning of the word "fairy".

> Fairy is very powerful. Even the bad author cannot escape it. He probably makes up his tale out of bits of older tales, or things he half-remembers, and they may be too strong for him to spoil or disenchant. Someone may meet them for the first time in his silly tale, and catch a glimpse of Fairy, and go on to better things. This could be put into a short story like this. There was once a cook, and he thought of making a cake for a children's party. His chief notion was that it must be very sweet . . .

"Then I stopped," he later wrote, "realizing that the 'short story' had developed a life of its own, and should be completed as a thing by itself."

Over the next two years during which *Smith of Wootton Major* was "completed as a thing by itself," Tolkien solved the problem. Instead of trying to explain Faery, he depicted it. He kept the image of the very sweet cake to symbolize the popular misunderstanding of Faery as saccharine and meant only for children. Balancing the allegorical cake, however, is the very real human whose entry into the enchanted realm allows him to "catch a glimpse" of Faery in all its mystery and severity and beauty. Triggered by the image of the cake, the story was initially and for much of its compositional life titled "The Great Cake", but as Tolkien's imagination shifted from the cake to the boy, he changed the title to reflect this more realistic approach, giving the story the name of its chief character.

Once he had abandoned the introduction to MacDonald's story in favour of his own tale, Tolkien bent himself to the task, and had roughed out a preliminary draft by early in the following year of 1965. In *Tolkien: a biography*, Humphrey Carpenter noted that *Smith* was "unusual" for Tolkien in being composed on the typewriter. This would be unusual indeed for the man who, when deprived of a pencil, compared himself to a hen without a beak. Carpenter's assumption was evidently based on a statement Tolkien had made to Clyde Kilby that a particular typed version of the story was "virtually the original" and was "never written out in Ms". The word "original" and the phrase "never written out" conveyed the not unreasonable impression that the story was composed *entirely* on the typewriter. However, even if we discount the several handwritten versions of the introduction, there was a partial stage, at least, of manuscript composition, an early version begun on the typewriter but continued in manuscript, a half-and-half, a hybrid draft.

The apparent discrepancy between the statement and the evidence may be resolved by a look at the word *virtually* in Tolkien's phrase, "virtually the original". *Virtual* means simply, "in effect, though not in actual fact". Since the typed "original" in question incorporated much previously handwritten material, it was undoubtedly "in effect" the first fully realized draft, and thus virtually the original. It is probable that it is this completed draft, which Tolkien called a "careless typescript, corrected and altered by hand", that was "never written out" in manuscript.

In addition, there exist three complete typewritten

single-spaced versions of the story. There is a preliminary full draft A, a corrected full copy B with marginal notes and emendations in ink, and a final fair copy C, with minor corrections to typos, and notes such as "leave space" [between paragraphs] obviously intended as instructions to a typesetter. Draft A is probably the virtual original Tolkien mentioned in his note to Kilby. It is headed "The Great Cake" although a later hand has written in marker pen, "Smith of Wootton" on the newspaper wrapping. Below this, the same hand (and pen) has noted, "full copy before final revision". Draft B, revised from draft A, and also headed "The Great Cake", contains the added episode of Smith's adventure with the Lake of Tears. In some of the early drafts of this incident, conceived separately to be inserted into the story, the lake is clearly liquid, so fluid that Smith can swim in it. In Draft B this was revised, with the lake surface now "harder than stone and slidder than glass". In draft C *slidder* is replaced by *sleeker*, and the lake is described in C, as in the published book, to be "sleeker than glass".

Draft C also introduces the change of title with a separate title page on which is typed, *Smith of Wootton Major*, with Tolkien's signature written below in ink. Serving as the cover sheet for C is a large stamped mailing envelope addressed to "Miss Incledon, Woodcocks,

AFTERWORD

Ditchling, Hassocks, Sussex". Tolkien had evidently sent a copy of the story to his cousin and contemporary Marjorie Incledon, elder daughter of his mother's sister May. A handwritten note on the envelope cover sheet identifies C as "Version as Read Blackfriars". Included with this version is a handwritten introduction addressed to an audience of, "any who may have come here expecting me to talk about poetry".

In a letter dated 28 October 1966 Tolkien described the Blackfriars evening to his grandson, Michael George, then a graduate student at Oxford. "I did not warn you of my talk on Wednesday night," he wrote. "I thought you would be too busy. I did not give a talk in fact, but read a short story recently written and yet unpublished; and that you can read when you have time: *Smith of Wootton Major*: if I have not already inflicted on you." The immediacy of the reference to "Wednesday night", suggests that the reading had taken place only shortly before, and indeed, 26 October 1966, two days before the date of the letter, was a Wednesday. As Tolkien described the evening,

> The event astonished me altogether, and also the promoters of the series: the Prior of Blackfriars and the Master of Pusey House. It was a nasty wet evening.

SMITH OF WOOTTON MAJOR

But such a concourse poured into Blackfriars that the Refectory (a long hall as long as a church) had to be cleared and could not contain it. Arrangements for relay to passages outside had to be hastily made. I am told that more than 800 people gained admittance. It became very hot, and I think you were better away. (*Letters*, pp.370–1)

In response to an inquiry about this event, a different perspective was offered by Father Bailey, at the time the Prior of Blackfriars, who had invited Tolkien to participate. Fr. Bailey wrote that,

So far as I remember there was no advertising, apart perhaps from a piece of paper at the church door. But the news spread, and the result was buses from London, Cambridge, & perhaps Leicester. The talk was given in the refectory, a large room, with a marble floor, from Portugal if I remember rightly, & seats round the walls. The seats were all occupied, & the floor covered with people sitting with legs bent. This meant that the cable from the point in the middle of the floor to his [Tolkien's] microphone at the top of the refectory, got upset, so people towards the back could not hear him. But no matter – they sat quietly gazing at him as tho' he was one of the apostles. To see him and look at him was enough (personal communication to the editor).

A second explanation for the difficulty of hearing the speaker was Tolkien's apology to his audience that he was "suffering from the aftermath of a sore throat." By late October of 1966, then, the story was essentially in its final form as published, for aside from the occasional proofreader's marginal corrections to typographical errors, the Blackfriars version conforms in all particulars to the later book.

Smith of Wootton Major was published in November 1967 by George Allen & Unwin Ltd. The book was a small format (14.7 × 10.5 cm) hardcover edition with illustrations by Pauline Baynes, who had done the illustrations for *Farmer Giles of Ham* and *The Adventures of Tom Bombadil*. In the same month, Tolkien's American publisher, Houghton Mifflin, published a slightly larger (16.2 × 10.8 cm) hardcover edition with the Baynes illustrations. Both editions were re-printed a number of times. The story was also published in the magazine *Redbook*, Issue # 130 (December 1967, pages 58–61 and 101, 103–7) with illustrations by Milton Glaser. In 1969 Ballantine Books brought out a combined paperback edition of *Smith of Wootton Major* and *Farmer Giles of Ham*. Allen & Unwin brought out a second hardcover edition of the story in 1975 and an American second appeared in 1978. New hardcover editions with illustrations by Roger Garland came out from Unwin Hyman in 1990 and Houghton Mifflin in 1991. In 1997, HarperCollins included it in *Tales from the Perilous Realm* (the other tales were *Farmer Giles of Ham*, *The Adventures of Tom Bombadil* and *Leaf by Niggle*). Together with *Tree and Leaf*, *Farmer Giles of Ham*, *The Adventures of Tom Bombadil* and *Sir Gawain and the Green Knight*, *Smith* was part of *A Tolkien Miscellany* published by the Science Fiction Book Club in 2002. And this is just the English-language editions. The story has been translated into Afrikaans, Dutch, German, Swedish, Japanese, Spanish, Catalan, Czech, Polish, Hebrew, Portuguese, Russian, Finnish, Italian, Serbo-Croat and French.

In contrast to the story's evident popular appeal, critical reaction to *Smith* was mixed. Writing in *Children's Libraries Newsletter*, 4, No. 2 (May 1968), Hugh Crago found the book to be not as good as Tolkien's longer fiction, and criticized the narrative for lacking humour, and its human characters for lacking "the glorious individuality" of hobbits. A different view was given by Christopher Derrick in *Tablet*, 222 (10 February

1968). Derrick called *Smith* a "sad, wise book" and "a myth of great delicacy". Frederick Lauritson in *Library Journal* 92 (15 November 1967) felt both plot and characters lacked depth. In the *National Review* for 7 May 1968 Jared Lobdell opined that while the book had "great moments" it was "a little *too* charming to bear re-reading". Reviewing it in the *New York Times Book Review* for 4 February 1968, Robert Phelps rightly termed it "an elegy", and described it as "a homely, haunting tale". In the *Horn Book* for February 1968, R.H. Vigures called the story "graceful, joyous, and beautiful".

Tolkien himself called it "an old man's book, already weighted with the presage of bereavement", and taking their cue from him, many have read Smith's surrender of the star as Tolkien's farewell to his art. Paul Kocher called the story its author's "Prospero speech", and Humphrey Carpenter saw in it Tolkien's "anxiety over the future and his growing grief at the approach of old age". While these elements are undeniably present, it would be a disservice to the book and its author to suppose that there was nothing more to the story than a long goodbye. In its own right and apart from any biographical considerations it stands as a true fairy story in Tolkien's terms – a story "about the *aventures* of men in the Perilous Realm" of Faërie, "the realm or state in which fairies have their being". That realm holds "the seas, the sun, the moon, the sky; and the earth, and all things that are in it: tree and bird, water and stone, wine and bread, and ourselves, mortal men, when we are enchanted."

Perhaps the best evaluator of the story's elusive yet affecting quality was Roger Lancelyn Green, who noted in the *Sunday Telegraph* for 3 December 1967 that, "To seek for the meaning is to cut open the ball in search of its bounce." Tolkien treasured the comment, and wrote Green to thank him. He also preserved, but not as a treasure, what is undoubtedly the most scathing commentary on the book, Christopher Williams's "Among a faery elite" in *New Society* for 7 December 1967. In its lofty disdain for Tolkien's aims, methods and final product, Williams's review rivals Edmund Wilson's "Oo! Those Awful Orcs!" appraisal of *The Lord of the Rings* in *Nation*, 182 (14 April 1956). Williams quoted sentences out of context, dismissed Tolkien's Faery as "the medievalist's version of a Cellophane flowerbed", and proclaimed the story's inappropriateness for "modern children". But just as *The Lord of the Rings* survived Edmund Wilson, so *Smith of Wootton Major* has survived Christopher Williams. It seems safe to predict that the beauty and mystery of Tolkien's story will continue to enchant and intrigue readers when its critics are long gone.

A particular aim of this edition has been to afford the reader a glimpse of the author at work, by appending to the story transcriptions of documents pertaining to its creation and development. Tolkien's explanation to Clyde Kilby of the genesis of the story, and the following transcription of his never-finished introduction to *The Golden Key* chart the progress of his invention from dissatisfaction with George MacDonald to the germ of his idea for his own story. The "Time Scheme and Characters", the "Suggestions for the ending", and the long, reflective essay "Smith of Wootton Major" convey the meticulously charted back-story and philosophical underpinning, the narrative's invisible but essential supporting structure.

The "Time Scheme and Characters" gives extended genealogies and histories for the chief inhabitants of Wootton Major. Concentrating in particular on the mysterious Grandfather Rider who leaves Wootton at the beginning of the story never to return, it supplies a year-by-year chronology that antedates the beginning of the story by some seventy years, and spans one hundred and twenty years and three generations of the characters' lives. Tolkien gave his characters – who plainly were as real to him as they were to one another – their proper names, family histories and relationships to one another and to the village. The same concern led to his "Suggestions for the ending of the story", its speculation on reasons for and wording of the Queen's message, and attention to the important relationship between Smith and his son, to the necessary absence of Smith's wife and daughter at the time of his final return from Faery, and to the dynamics of the final interview between the Apprentice and Nokes.

The long essay called, like the story itself, "Smith of Wootton Major", examines the physical environment of the village as well as its moral and spiritual condition as the story opens. The essay describes its crafts, especially the importance of cooking in the life of the village; maps its relationship to the Wood and to the smaller villages of Wootton Minor and Walton within the Wood; and examines at length the vital though implicit relationship between the inhabitants of the human and the Faery worlds.

Finally, three facsimile documents supply evidence of the creation-revision process. The hybrid draft, unfortunately missing two pages, nevertheless gives the story in what is probably its earliest complete version, for it concludes with the last interview between the Apprentice and old Nokes. The first half of this draft is typed, while the second half, continuing an uninterrupted train of thought, is written out in pen. This draft contains elements that, though subsequently removed, nevertheless left their impress on the tale. First is the object that goes into the cake, which in the typewritten pages is not a star but a ring. By the manuscript continuation the ring had changed to the star that it remained from then on. But whether ring or star, the presence of a true faerian artifact was the necessary counterweight to the other artifact, the very sweet cake that represents the Cook's notion of *fairy*.

Second is the smith's epithet. When the King encounters the smith in Faery, he addresses him as "Gilthir", and the narrative adds "for that was his name (Starbrow) in Fairy: at home he was called Alfred Smithson". Like the ring, the Fairy name *Gilthir* disappears, for in all subsequent drafts of this episode the smith is addressed simply as "Starbrow", as in the final published version. The name *Alfred*, shortened to *Alf*, was given to the Apprentice for whom the equation Alf = Elf was more appropriate.

Two other facsimiles, a manuscript and a typed version of the inserted "Lake of Tears" episode, illustrate how Tolkien expanded *Smith of Wootton Major* from the inside. Added at the time of draft B and retained in C, the scene was developed through four stages of composition, two very rough single-page manuscript versions, one clear but incomplete handwritten copy reproduced in this volume and a final single-page typewritten draft, also reproduced in this volume. The trajectory of the story remained consistent from the beginning, but the narrative design was elaborated by added details and episodes.

This added material affords the reader an extended look at the creative process, showing Tolkien literally thinking on paper, and allowing the reader to follow the authorial progression from explanation to inspiration to formulation to painstaking revision, bringing both *Smith of Wootton Major* and its author to life.

Verlyn Flieger

"Genesis of the story"
Tolkien's Note to Clyde Kilby

Possibly the most interesting item, revealing the genesis of the story.

Sometime during 1964 I agreed with 'Pantheon Books' to write a preface to G. MacDonald's <u>Golden Key</u>, which they proposed to issue as a 'fairy-tale' for children. No doubt I was approached because I mentioned G. M. (and <u>The G. Key</u> in particular) with praise, in <u>Tree and Leaf</u> p. 26 (American Edn.). But I found that a highly selective memory had retained only a few impressions of things that moved me, and re-reading G. M. critically filled me with distaste. I had of course, never thought of <u>The G. K.</u> as a story for children (though apparently G. McD did). The task thus proved distasteful to me; but I was relieved of it by collapse of the project (and for all I know perhaps of "Pantheon Books"[)].

When striving to say some useful things in a preface, I found it necessary to deal with the term "fairy"

– always necessary nowadays, whether talking to children or adults: cf. Jack's letter of October 9, 1954 in the recent collection.

In the course of this I tried to give an illustration of "Faery", and said: "this could be put into a 'short story' like this" – and then proceeded in what is a first version of <u>Smith of W.M.</u> pp. 11–20. There I stopped, realizing that the 'short story' had developed an independent life and should be completed as a thing in itself. If I had gone on I should only have written a severely critical or 'anti' essay on G. M. – unnecessary, and a pity since G.M. has performed great services for other minds – such as Jack's. But he was evidently born loving (moral) allegory, and I was born with an instinctive distaste for it. "Phantastes" wakened him, and afflicted me with profound dislike. It is better anyway to preach by example than by criticism of others. But <u>Smith</u> remains as it were "an anti-G.M. tract". There is <u>no</u> allegory in the Faery, which is conceived as having a real extramental existence. [There is some trace of allegory in the Human part, which seems to me obvious though no reader or critic has yet adverted to it. As usual there is no 'religion' in the story; but plainly enough the Master Cook and the Great Hall etc are a (somewhat satirical) allegory of the village-church, and village parson: its functions steadily decaying and losing all touch with the 'arts', into mere eating and drinking – the last traces of anything 'other' being left to children.]

Tolkien's draft introduction to *The Golden Key*

DON'T READ THIS! Not yet.

This is a famous fairy tale. I hope you will like it. That is all that needs to be said, as an 'introduction': Reader meet the Golden Key.

I never read what are called 'introductions' to tales, 'fairy' or not: long talks about the author or the story; and I do not think that anybody should. It is not fair to the author or to the reader. The author meant to speak direct to his reader, and did not want any one else to interfere, telling the reader to notice this or that, or to understand that or this, before the tale had even begun. You should be free to notice and like (or dislike) this and that for yourselves at first, without help or (very probably) hindrance. So do not pay any attention to me. At any rate until you have read the tale. For what is wrong with 'introductions' is their place. They should come second and not first and be called 'postlections' or after-readings, and be like the talks a reader might have with other people who have read the tale; they might lead to sharing of pleasure, or to debate on disagreements; and so lead even to a second reading.

After all would it not be rather rude as well as a nuisance, if I said: 'Dear Reader may I introduce you to George MacDonald? I expect you will notice his beautiful beard, though you must remember that men wore beards in his day, big ones, though his was bigger and better than most. Look at his amazing clothes: his scarlet cloak, his marvellous waistcoat with dozens of gilt buttons, and his jewellery! But you should see him in full Highland Scottish dress with kilt and plaid and dirk. But of course you have noticed his Scottish accent and his name, and that will explain it. All the same I must warn you that he is a preacher, not only on the platform or in the pulpit; in all his many books he preaches, and it is his preaching that is valued most by the grown-up people who admire him most.'

I think it would be better just to leave you and George MacDonald alone for a while for a walk or a talk together and let you find out first what you could for yourselves with your own eyes and ears.

But of course the talk would be brief, just as The Gol[d]en Key though it is one of the best things that MacDonald wrote is short. And after the reading or the meeting there might be questions that you would like to ask. People are puzzling after a short acquaintance, and remarkable people very puzzling; and so are their writings. It might be interesting then to hear what some one else has to say, some one who perhaps knew the man, or his books better or for a longer while. If it is interesting and if you want to hear more, then read this. If not do not trouble.

If you are the kind of reader that MacDonald was really addressing and have read The Golden Key, you will not forget it. Something at least will remain in your own mind, as a beautiful or strange or alarming picture and will grow there, and its meaning, or one of its meanings – its meaning for you – will unfold itself, as you also grow. For me the chief picture that remained was the great valley encircled by hard towering mountains, with its smooth floor on which the shadows played, the sea of shadows cast by things that could not themselves be seen. When I went back to the story after some years, I was surprised to find what a lot more there was in it that I had forgotten. But it still remains for me the centre of the tale. I now find that it has of course stirred the imagination of other readers, though it does not seem to all of them as important as to me; nor does it have the same 'meaning' for them as for me. But that does not trouble me. These pictures or visions that come in such tales are large and alive and no one who sees them, not even the writer himself, understands the whole of them. Just so with people (even small people) or with countries (even counties) [;] they are too large, too full of various things, for even old friends or inhabitants to agree in their views about them. And when it comes to Fairy-land! That has no known limits, and no maps. Travellers have to do without them – probably the best thing. For if they make some for themselves, they will lose them, or find that they are no use when they return, especially if that is by a different road.

But since MacDonald himself called The Golden Key a fairy tale, I think something should be said about 'fairy'.

If a thing is called a 'fairy tale', the first point to note is 'tale'. Whatever you put in front: plain, fairy, historical, ghost, scientific, cautionary, moral, or simply funny, the tale should tell something; a story, of related events, which should interest a listener in themselves but especially as they are arranged in a sequence from the chosen beginning to the chosen end. I say 'chosen', meaning 'by the inventor', because the beginning and end of a story is to it like the edges of the canvas or an

TOLKIEN'S DRAFT INTRODUCTION

added frame to a picture, say a landscape. It concentrates the teller's attention, and yours, on one small part of the country. But there are of course no real limits: under the earth, and in the sky above, and in the remote and faintly glimpsed distances, and in the unrevealed regions on either side, there are things that influence the very shape and colour of the part that is pictured. Without them it would be quite different, and they are really necessary to understanding what is seen.

Still if we look at the picture, or listen to the tale, we should be held by it; we should want to hear it all (perhaps more than once), we should enjoy hearing it, before we even begin to think why. If not the Tale has failed (for us). The word put in front does not matter much, though it may help you from the beginning to read in the right mood. But it may also be misleading. Tales like the people who write them are not easy to label or be described by a single word. Earnest people (preachers for instance) can also be humorous; scientific people can and sometimes do write poetry and even fairy tales. Also you may even come to dislike certain labels, and avoid anything that has one of them attached to it: like sermon, or medicine, and say 'not for me' without even tasting first.

In many ways the most important and also most

misleading label is <u>fairy</u>. For one thing, the label is often nowadays misused, and 'specially suitable for children' is often added to 'fairy-tale'; and that is enough to put off any child (whatever ages that word is supposed to cover). Though it is actually a compliment to 'fairy tales', since real children are generally good judges of tales as tales: whether they carry you along and make you want to go on listening or reading. It was George MacDonald's own children who first heard <u>Alice in Wonderland</u> read from manuscript, and Lewis Carroll published it because it had delighted them.

For another thing, 'fairy' is often misunderstood. It was once a 'big word', including many marvellous things, but it has in ordinary use dwindled, so that I suppose to many people 'fairy' now means first of all a little creature, like a tiny human being, pretty or impish, which is usually invisible to us. But 'fairy-tales' are not just stories in which imaginary creatures of this kind appear. Many do not mention them at all. In many others where they do appear (such as <u>The Golden Key</u>) they are not important. You will have noticed that although George MacDonald wrote this tale nearly 100 years ago, he himself spoke already of 'the little creatures commonly called fairies', but added 'though there are many different kinds of fairies in Fairyland'.

TOLKIEN'S DRAFT INTRODUCTION

He might have said 'older, more powerful and important kinds' but he leaves that for the readers to find out, if they do not already know it.

The truth is – I only mention this bit of history because it is impossible to understand the meaning of 'fairy' without knowing it – the truth is that fairy did not originally mean a 'creature' at all, small or large. It meant enchantment or magic, and the enchanted world or country in which marvellous people lived, great and small, with strange powers of mind and will for good and evil. There all things were wonderful: earth, water, air, and fire, and all living and growing things, beasts and birds, and trees and herbs were strange and dangerous, for they had hidden powers and were more than they seemed to be to mortal eyes. So when fairy was put in front of another word (used as an adjective), as in fairy wand, or tale, or godmother, or in Fairy Queen and Fairyland, it did not mean (and still does not) 'a pretty little fairy'. It means powerful, magical, belonging to Fairy or coming from that strange world. The Fairy Queen was not a queen shaped like a little fairy, but the Queen of Fairy, a great and dangerous person, however beautiful, Queen of the enchanted world and all its people. A fairy tale is a tale about that world, a glimpse of it; if you read it, you enter Fairy with the author as your guide. He may be a bad guide or a good one: bad if he does not take the adventure seriously, and is just 'spinning a yarn' which he thinks is good enough 'for children'; good, if he knows something about Fairy, and has himself caught some glimpses of it which he is trying to put into words. But Fairy is very powerful. Even the bad guide cannot escape it. He probably makes up his tale out of bits of older tales, or things he half remembers, and they may be too strong for him to spoil or disenchant. Some one may meet them for the first time in his silly tale, and catch a glimpse of Fairy and go on to better things.

This could be put into a 'short story' like this. There was once a cook, and he thought of making a cake for a children's party. His chief notion was that it must be very sweet, and he meant to cover it all over with sugar-icing [*here the text breaks off*]

'The Great Cake'
Time Scheme and Characters

Characters

A. Alf, mysterious Apprentice appointed by G. Called by most people <u>Prentice</u>. Later became MC (Master Cook). Finally revealed as the King of Faery, who lived in the village for 58 years (for purposes of his own) but not, it may be supposed, without ever visiting his own realm in that time.

*E. Ella, daughter of G. She married OS and was the mother of S.

G. 'Grandfather'. His name was Rider. After an adventurous youth he married R and settled down. Later he became Apprentice to the then MC, and eventually MC himself. He was the maternal grandfather of S.

H. Harper. He eventually succeeded A as MC.

N. Nokes. He succeeded G as MC, since no one better could be found when G (who had never appointed

an apprentice) went off suddenly and did not return.
NT. Nokes of Townsend, his grandson (see T).
NS, NDS, see S.

*R. Rose Sangster, a beautiful girl of a distant village, brought home as his wife by G. Died in giving birth to E.

Q. The Queen of Faery. She only appears as seen by S in Faery.

S. Smith. The chief person in the tale. Became the best iron-smith in the village and country round. Received the 'fay star' at the Feast, and became a traveller in Faery. His name (probably Ned like his son's) is not recorded. He was called <u>Starbrow</u> in Faery.

NS. Nell (Webster) his wife. NDS. Nan (Smith's daughter) his daughter and eldest child. OS. Old Smith, his father, whom he succeeded. YS. Young Smith, his son Ned.

T. Tim, son of Nokes of Townsend, and so Nokes' great-grandson. His mother was W sister of NS the Smith's wife. He inherited the star.

*W. Wyn (Webster) sister of NS, and mother of NT.

Those marked * are not mentioned by name in the story as told, but would be important in a full tale. Two

'THE GREAT CAKE' TIME SCHEME AND CHARACTERS

other persons also briefly appear: TW Tom (Wright) of Wootton Minor, who married Nan Smith's daughter; and Tomling his son, the smith's grandchild. Four children, also present at the feast when S received the star, are named: beside Nell (NS), Miller's Molly, Cooper's Harry, and Draper's Lily.

SMITH OF WOOTTON MAJOR

Dates

Since no human person older than G appears in the story, for showing the sequence of events and the ages of the various actors the dates are reckoned from the year of G's birth, which is arbitrarily taken as 1000.

Year

1000 G born.
1018 G goes off on his 'travels' and only returns at irregular intervals to Wootton Major, until 1035.
1027 OS born.
1030 N born.
1035 G marries R and returns with her to Wootton Major.
1037 E daughter of G and R is born. R dies. G becomes a grave and taciturn man.
1038 The MC's apprentice is killed in an accident. G offers to help him and learn the craft. He is given a trial and quickly becomes accomplished.
1044 G becomes MC.
1048 G manages a Twenty-four Feast with notable success. Though he takes no part himself, he re-introduces singing and dancing (long neglected) as part of the children's merrymaking.

'THE GREAT CAKE' TIME SCHEME AND CHARACTERS

1052   N, a young man of no craft, though he fancies his skill in many, offers himself to G as assistant. N is allowed to help at busy times, but as soon as he has learned a little he thinks he knows all. G dislikes him and after a time will not employ him any more. G refuses to appoint any apprentice from among the young men of the village.

1055   N marries a wife with some money. He does nothing in particular, but cooks as a 'hobby'.

1062   E at 25 marries OS who is ten years older. He had been regarded as a confirmed bachelor 'too busy with his work to think about marrying'. In the spring immediately after the wedding G goes off for a 'holiday'. His daughter E, an excellent cook, manages the Kitchen in his absence and declines the help of N. G returns in good time for the Winter Feast. He brings with him A, as his apprentice, to general surprise: A looks no older than about 12 to 13. G is now a much merrier man. It may be guessed that he had returned to Faery for a visit.

1063   S born in June.

1065   N (Nell Webster) born, also in June. In the autumn G goes off again and announces that he will not return. He leaves A in charge. (He deposits a small silver star in a black spice-box in the store-room.) The Village Council will not make A Master Cook, he seems a mere boy. For want of any better they appoint N as MC. A remains as N's apprentice.

1072 A Twenty-four Feast occurs again. N puts the silver star in the Great Cake among other coins and trinkets, but A in fact makes most of the Cake and all its decorations. S and N[ell] are two of the children present. S swallows the star but does not know it.

1073 S discovers the silver star at dawn on his tenth birthday in June.

1078 S begins to assist his father OS in the forge and shows extraordinary talent.

1079 H born.

1090 N now very fat and lazy retires at 60. For a long time A has done practically all his work, as many in the village guess. A, now appearing to be a man over 40, is appointed MC.

1091 S marries Nell. S is 28, Nell 26. Their marriage probably delayed by the journeys of S to Faery and the need for him to take over more and more of his father's work. It would seem that S went little to Faery for some years immediately after his marriage, and not beyond the borders. His long journeys in Faery probably were undertaken mostly in the years between 1098 and 1108, and 1115–20.

1093 NDS (Nan) born, in May.

1095 A appoints H as his apprentice.

1096 YS (Ned) born in the spring. In the winter a Twenty-four Feast is held. It was the first managed by A, and was praised as 'the best that is remembered'.

1104 OS dies (77).

1105 E the wife of OS dies. S and his family move from a small house nearby into the Old Smithy House. It stands on the West Road, the last house in the village on that side.

1108 S returns from a long visit to Faery, bringing the Living Flower given him by the dancing maiden.

1112 Tim son of NT born in March.

1117 Nan marries Tom Wright of Wootton Minor: a remote kinsman (3rd cousin), being a descendant of G's mother's sister.

1118 Tomling, Nan's child and the grandson of S, is born in the autumn.

1120 S makes his last journey in Faery and meets the Queen. He is overtaken by A on the way back. He surrenders the star to A, who places it in the black box. A pays a visit to old N. Twenty-four Feast held. The star passes to Tim. A announces his departure. H becomes MC in the first days of 1121.

Suggestions for the ending of the story

The Fairy Apprentice (who it is evidently suggested was in fact the King, on an 'adventure' or mission in the mortal world) must have had himself an apprentice: the situation of the Cook going off and leaving no successor cannot be repeated. Some mention must be made of this earlier in the story. Who was the apprentice? Not the Smith's son. For that would have brought the Fairy Ap. into close connexion with the smith. Not of course any 'elvish' person again. Either nothing should be made of the choice of the app. to follow the Fairy Ap. or it should be some one significant. Perhaps Old Nokes' son?

When the Smith comes home after surrendering the star, should any more be said than has been about what became of him? In earlier draft it is said that he <u>could</u> go back to Fayery, for the mark of the star that had been on his brow was still visible to the folk of Fayery; but he could not go deep in, nor ever visit any new place or see any new thing that he had not already seen. (This has a significance, of course: a time comes for writers and artists, when invention and 'vision' cease and they can only reflect on what they have seen and learned.) But that is not the whole point of the tale. Which includes sacrifice, and the handing on, with trust and without keeping a hand on things, of power and vision to the next generation. Also another point is that the visions of imagination are not enough; they are only pictures and intimations. When wisdom comes the mind though enriched by imagination, having learned or seen distantly truths only perceptible in this way, must prepare to leave the world of Men and of Fayery.

In the scene at the forge, where the son is obviously taking up his father['s] work in the world of Men though his intimations of 'Fayery' will never go beyond what he has received at secondhand from his father – what about the wife and daughter? I feel that there should be no one in the house but son and father. But the wife cannot have died – something would have to have been said of that before. It easiest to say nothing. And best? But I think a commonplace very 'mortal' and domestic note should be struck, making the adventures in Fayery seem very remote, yes, even absurd.

SUGGESTIONS FOR THE ENDING OF THE STORY

?The daughter should have married – perhaps a man in another village. The wife called away unexpectedly to the birth of her first child, the smith's first grandchild.

What shall be the message to the King? And what shall it mean? <u>You are awaited</u>. This might sound like an order to return. But the King's supremacy must be maintained. If not it must be just a wife's message to an absent husband: which is not the kind of thing to be sent by such a messenger. OR if important and urgent it must refer to the realm of Fayery and its government, and to matters beyond mortal concern. In any case the Queen must have known at least where to find the King, and could have sent a swifter and better-informed messenger. <u>The time has come</u>. This could be reasonably interpreted. As a message which in fact concerned the smith. It could say to the King, if he received it, that the Queen had seen and examined the smith, and was now of opinion that it was time for him to relinquish the star. (An opinion which probably the King already held and possibly the Queen had not: he awaited the outcome of her interview, perhaps, and her opinion.) This message would be sent by the smith himself, because he was concerned, and because he was returning at once to the place where the King was. The Queen said 'if you meet him'. She did not know whether the smith would recognize him at last. She need not have known that the King would contrive a meeting just within the borders of Fayery, where recognition was more likely. If the smith had recognized him, there would be no further doubt that 'the time had come'.

It is intended to be suggested that the smith did not consciously recognize the King as such. He had always been vaguely aware that the 'Apprentice' was a special person, and now knew that he at least also walked in Fayery; dimly he now felt that he had some authority in connexion with the star – but no more. But the King had induced him to part with the star without the use of command or authority, as an act of generosity.

It is probable that the delivery of the message should be brought in earlier. The King's wisdom would then be shown in contriving the surrender in this way, instead of by revealing himself. Somewhat so.

After '. . . how to deal with the star'.

They said no more and went on their way together. They had passed the confines of Fayery and were drawing near to the village when suddenly the smith stopped. 'Master Cook', he said, 'something . . .' and so 'the time has come'.

SUGGESTIONS FOR THE ENDING OF THE STORY

Continue. 'I understand. Go home now in peace.'

They walked on again until they came at last to the village hall, and in the world the sun was setting and a red light was in the windows; the gilded carvings on the great door glowed.* The Cook opened a small door at the back and led the smith down a dark passage into the store-room. He lit a tall candle, unlocked a cupboard and took down from a shelf the black box.

Continue as in version till '. . . in a clear sky close to the moon.'
Now write: Then he took a deep breath and started on his way; but he looked back once and he saw the Apprentice Cook standing tall in the narrow door way watching him. They each raised a hand in farewell.

In the gathering dusk he walked now quickly to his own house. . .

The message would however in any case speed the King's departure. His errand was accomplished – or would be when the star passed on to some other child. After the next Great Party, in 3 months time – it was

---

* this hall had been redecorated by the New Cook at his own expense

now early October, he would soon go, leaving the apprentice in charge.

Question: Should the tale end with the rather absurd episode of the Apprentice having a conversation with the fat conceited Old Nokes? The original idea was that it should be the king-cook, who was before he left Nokes revealed to Nokes, but this had no effect on him, and was attributed to a dream after a good dinner. ? It might be the new Apprentice, who had knowledge of the placing of the star back in the box by the smith from the king-cook. (But this would cut out the comic details of the remembrances of the Party of the Star, which are really its point.)

?Should it be told to whom the star passed I think not.

Smith of Wootton Major essay

[This essay has been transcribed to conform as closely as possible to Tolkien's typescript, wherein he interpolated secondary information as notes within the text, writing them as the ideas occurred to him, often in mid-paragraph, sometimes in mid-sentence. His device for distinguishing notes was to type the notes in red, so that they stand out from the text while yet being fully embedded within it. Here, the notes have been reproduced in the same position as Tolkien originally wrote them, but in grey and in a smaller typeface.]

This short tale is not an 'allegory', though it is capable of course of allegorical interpretations at certain points. It is a 'Fairy Story', of the kind in which beings that may be called 'fairies' or 'elves' play a part and are associated in action with human people, and are regarded as having a 'real' existence, that is one in their own right and independent of human imagination and invention. It is cast in an imaginary (but English) country-side, before the advent of power-machinery, but in a time when a prosperous community, mainly of craftsmen with an agricultural environment, could be aware of and afford imported luxuries such as sugar and spices. It is suggested that this prosperity, based on the industry and skill of most of the community, had begun to have an effect in making many of them vulgarly self-satisfied, and coarser. Thus it is evident that at the time the tale opens 'festivals' were mainly celebrated by eating and drinking; dancing, singing and tale-telling were little thought of. There is no mention of musical instruments, except in the name of Harper (which as will be seen is significant). The Great Hall is no longer painted or adorned.

The geographical relations of Wootton and Faery are inevitably, but also intentionally left vague. In such stories there must be some way or ways of access from and to Faery, available at least to Elves as to favoured mortals. But it is also necessary that Faery and the World (of Men), though in contact, should occupy a different time and space, or occupy them in different modes. Thus though it appears that the Smith can enter Faery more or less at will (being specially favoured), it is evident that it is a land, or world of unknown limits, containing seas and mountains; also it is plain that even during a brief visit (such as one on an evening walk) he can spend a great deal longer in Faery than his absence counts in the world; on his long journeys an absence from home of, say, a week is sufficient for exploration and experiences in Faery equivalent to months or even years.

As far as geography goes, Faery is situated (or its entrances are) westward. 'From Far Easton to Westwood' denotes the bounds of the world to the villagers: from the most eastern village of people of their own kind to the Forest, yet uncultivated, immediately to the West. Wootton thus represents an earlier intrusion of men's settlements into the foreign country of Forest; Wootton Minor is still a village in a clearing. The Forest is still close to the western edge of Wootton Major. The smithy is at the extreme western edge of it (if you like because of the need of wood fuel). It is at any rate thus made easier for the Smith to go into the Forest unobserved by any but his household, or to go on journeys 'on business', without his movements being the matter of gossip.

In many Fairy Tales use is made of the idea that time passes quickly in Faery, so that a man who finds his way there may come out after what seems a brief episode to find that years, even centuries have passed. Except as a mere device to bring a man out of the past into contact with a (to him) future time – that is in a tale of which this is the real point, and Faery as such is not seriously considered – I have always felt this to be a mistake: a mistake in credibility, if Faery of any kind is taken seriously. It is true that the seeming time in Faery being immensely longer than it is felt to be is usually told of mortals that intrude into Faery. It is also true that in some actual experiences the time they take may seem short, and be found to be much longer when contact is made with ordinary affairs again. This occurs especially after absorption (mainly of intense interest and also usually pleasure) in some such things as reading, seeing plays, revelry or meetings with friends. I have often said that this idea must have originated in inns: for nowhere does time 'fly' so fast compared with daily experience as when sitting and drinking and conversing with dear friends in an inn. I am sure there is some truth in this. But there are other experiences. Notably that of dreams, in which a long (or full) experience may be found to have occupied a short time in the extra-mental world. 'Narrative' is perhaps the only common measure. What takes a long time to relate adequately is long. (I mean: relate, if one wishes to, or has to, relate it. A diarist who enters against one day 'nothing to relate' probably means nothing that interests me, or nothing of the kind that I usually record for future reference.) 'O minutes great as years!' Dream is perhaps a better analogy for the purpose. But also this must be considered: the Faery of this tale is a particular one. If one accepts it, while 'within' the tale, then clearly the Rulers of Faery – who are presented as interested in Men (not necessarily primarily) and beneficently – must be able to arrange that the experiences in Faery of favoured human persons may be enjoyed without dislocation of their normal human life. The time of their Faery must be different, even though it may be at points contiguous. For them human time is or may be also longer than that of Faery. The King dwells in Wootton for 58 years.

As for place. Entry into the 'geographical' bounds of Faery also involves entry into Faery Time. How does a mortal 'enter' the geographical realm of Faery? Evidently not in dream or illusion. Physical objects, such as the star, the Living Flower, and the elvish toy, survive transplantation from Faery to the World. It is common in Fairy tales for the entrance to the fairy world to be presented as a journey underground, into a hill or mountain or the like. The origins of this do not concern me here. They lie largely in necrological imagination. But as used they are often mere 'rationalizations' – like the diminution in the size of 'elves' – a way of providing for a land of marvels within the same geography as that of Men. They are no more credible and no more interesting than Edgar Rice Burroughs tales dealing with a vast subterranean world. To me they kill the very kind of 'literary belief' that they are supposed to produce.

My symbol is not the underground, whether necrological and Orphic or pseudo-scientific in jargon, but the Forest: the regions still immune from human activities, not yet dominated by them (dominated! not conquered!). If Faery Time is at points contiguous with ours, the contiguity will also occur in related points in space – or that is the theory for the purpose of the story. At certain points at or just within the Forest borders a human person may come across these contiguous points and there enter F. time and space – if fitted to do so or permitted to do so. Within the relatively short time of the story (or indeed of several generations of Men in its suggested 'historical' background) these points will remain recognizable and able to be re-visited by those who have once found them. Going deep or far into Faery from such points represents a passing further and further away from a familiar or anthropocentric world. But in this tale Forest and Tree remain dominant symbols. They occur in three of the

SMITH OF WOOTTON MAJOR ESSAY

four 'remembered' and recorded experiences of the Smith – before his leave-taking of the Queen. They do not occur in the first, because it is at that point that he discovers that Faery is 'limitless' and is mainly involved in vast regions and events that do not concern Men and are impenetrable by them.

The situation in the village of Wootton is evidently of this sort. It was governed for local purposes by a council – probably a group of the heads of the chief and most prosperous 'crafts'. The crafts were still traditional and largely heritable: handed down from father to sons, or women to daughters; though where no children or none of sufficient aptitude were available a craftsman or craftswoman might take on an 'apprentice' and that would normally mean inclusion in the household and family. There were no proper surnames. The names Smith, Cooper, Miller, Wright, Weaver, (Webster for women), Stonewright (Mason) and the like indicated that their bearers actually practised that craft, or in a few cases that trade: such as, in a prosperous village, dealers in 'imported' goods, such as Draper or Spicer or Chandler.* Children are given simple names, placed after the name

*Nokes is a deliberate exception. He has a 'geographical' name (living by the oak). He does

> not belong to a craft. It would appear that he has 'means', that is probably owns some land outside the village, and comes from the peasant or farming folk in the surrounding country. In such a case, or in the case of crafts practised by several people or families, additional definitions might be added: such as "(of) Townsend", i.e. living in the last house, at one end or other of the main street.

of their father's craft, or sometimes in the case of girls after their mothers such as 'the Webster's Fanny'. The names chosen are simple abbreviated names, showing little relation to their original forms: Ned, Tim, Tom, Nell, Nan, etc. This allows the use of <u>Alf</u> for the elvish apprentice. (This name is evidently applied to him by the Master Cook who introduced him.)

Cooking was an exception. Though a recognized and esteemed skill, it was not practised as a family craft, nor generally as a livelihood. There was nothing corresponding to eating-houses. Strangers on business could get food and lodging at the one Inn: it was called by no other name at this time, though over the door could still be seen a carved stone, much defaced by time, bearing apparently a representation of three trees and the inscription <u>Welcō to þe Wode</u>. But it was not used by the villagers. Domestic cooking was done in the home, by women and men – by women mostly unless they were busy craftswomen. But Master Cook was a public official, and important. He was maintained out of public funds, as were the supplies for public feasts. His office was not hereditary; he was chosen as far as possible by taste and talent. This and the succession was normally provided for by the MC choosing an apprentice in good time to train him before he retired. The apprentice was of course usually a youth of the village: several as a rule applied for the apprenticeship, since the office was an enviable one and with it went the Cook's House adjoining the Hall. Though the waiting time before succession might be very long. The MC might retire at any time after he was satisfied with the attainments of the apprentice; but he could not be forced to retire, and was often reluctant to do so, although a decent pension and a comfortable cottage was provided. When he did retire, however, the Apprentice succeeded without debate, except in very unusual circumstances.*

> *One such set of circumstances occurs in the tale: the death or departure of the MC before he had appointed an apprentice, or before the a. was regarded as trained or old enough for the responsibility. The behaviour of Grandfather Rider when the tale begins

was altogether exceptional and odd. But it was possible for accidents to happen to an Apprentice. Actually Grandfather R. owed his position to such an accident (as well as his own versatile talents). The A. of the previous MC (who was already old and thinking of retirement) was killed by a falling tree on a day of violent storm not long before the Winter Feast. Rider offered his help in the emergency, and soon proved so clever that a few years later the MC was able to retire and hand over to him.

This 'Grandfather Rider', who seems to have set going the events that occupy this tale, was evidently a remarkable and peculiar person. His name was Rider, indicating that he was not a member or practiser of one of the chief 'crafts'. The Riders were interested in horses and their livelihood was obtained, in addition to the training of horses and horse-doctoring, by acting as the equivalents of a local post and carrier service. They would take messages or letters of urgency and sometimes convey packages to other villages and homesteads, especially those at a distance, often returning with similar errands. This part of their work especially suited Rob, his father's youngest son. He took largely after his mother, a Piper of Wootton Minor, and was restless and adventurous. He began errand-riding when he was little more than fifteen. He soon became known for the speed and accuracy with which he would take messages or perform errands, and for his reluctance to return and report. After a time he ceased to live in Wootton Major, and only returned there at irregular intervals as suited him; he became a 'traveller', a man of no fixed abode or livelihood. During this time though there were many rumours current nothing was really known about his journeys and adventures, until one day he came back, apparently provided with money and certainly with a wife. She was a young and beautiful woman called Rose, one of the Sangsters of Walton a distant village beyond Wootton Minor. She was much his junior, for by that time he must have been at least thirty-five.

Two years later their daughter Ella was born, but her mother died in childbirth. Rider, who had already seemed to those who remembered him as a boy changed into a quiet and thoughtful man, now became sad and taciturn. He was seldom seen abroad by day, but was sometimes met walking alone by those who were out late or very early before daybreak. The next year was one long remembered in Wootton as an ill year, beginning in great snowstorms and continuing violent and stormy until its end. Early in December there was great wind which did much damage in the village and threw down many old trees. The apprentice of the then Master Cook was of much the same age as Rider, a man called Wright, competent and well-liked, and expecting (and expected) soon to become Master Cook, since the old Cook intended to retire before long. Unfortunately Wright was on his way home from the Kitchen just at sundown when a great gust felled an old ash-tree that stood near his house, and he was crushed and killed in its fall.

There was grief in the village, and the old Master Cook was dismayed, for the Winter Feast was approaching and he had no competent help. The next day Rider came to the Kitchen and gave all the help he could to the old man. Before the evening everything there was in better order than it had been for years, and new plans for the ordering of the Feast were drawn up. As he prepared to go home Rider said: 'Another pair of hands is useful, Master. If mine are any good in your grief and trouble, say so, and I will be with you as long as you need me.'

So it came about that Rider entered the service of the Cook. To his surprise and that of all the village (for no rumour had at any rate mentioned anything in his roving life that might have given him an opportunity for learning the craft) Rider showed not only much knowledge but great talent for learning more speedily. The Winter Feast went off well, and before the next one it was understood that Rider was accepted as regular apprentice. When the Cook finally retired some six years after Wright's death, there was no question about the succession, and Rider became Master Cook. He remained a taciturn man, rather sad in face, though brisk in movement. He was not surly or unfriendly, but took evident pleasure in pleasing, and delighted by the gaiety of others, though he took little part in it. His mind seemed to be elsewhere, if it was possible to say that of one who attended to everything in his duties so promptly and with such skill. The Twenty-four Feast which occurred four years after he became Master was notable, indeed it was said to be the best that had been held in living memory. And the gayest. For singing and dancing were reintroduced, after long neglect, as part of the entertainment.

The remainder of the history of Rider's time as Master Cook is referred to in the tale. When he was fifty-two he still had appointed no apprentice, and that began to give some concern. Not that help was yet needed. Rider was active and more than capable; and his daughter Ella was also a very good cook and often helped with private family parties or at times of pressure during Feasts. For all minor services, washing, cleaning, preparing, waiting and the like, the Master Cook could of course always find plenty of assistance. It was the matter of the succession that troubled the Council. It was at this time that a young man called Nokes applied to be taken on. Rider did not take to him, but because of the pressure on him to begin training a successor he gave him a trial. He knew something about cooking, though not nearly as much as he supposed. He was difficult to teach, for he was not a quick learner, and did not like being corrected. If he found a thing difficult, he soon gave it up, and then affected to regard it as unimportant: 'just a fal-lal' as he was fond of saying, 'may please some, but there's no great call for it'. Rider did *not* appoint him apprentice. For a while he was called into help at very busy times, but soon Rider dropped him altogether.

No doubt it was due to his experience of Nokes (in part: there may have been other reasons) that Rider became so obstinate, and resisted all pressure to find an apprentice for a good many years. He had none when he decided to go on his unexpected holiday, although he was then sixty-two and had been MC for 18 years. He went in the spring, immediately after his daughter's wedding to Smith (in full Joe Smith of West-side*); so that the busiest time of the year was ahead, although the great Spring Feast was over. But Ella was able to take on the cooking work, and had the help of friends. She refused to have anything to do with Nokes, whom she disliked. (It was rumoured that Nokes, 'trying to find a side-door to the Kitchen' as gossips put it, had proposed marriage to her a few years before.

> *He was so called because there were several Smiths in the village; but Joe was the son of the chief of the craft, owner of the ancient Old Smithy on the western outskirts of the village. Joe was devoted to his craft and to his father who rather dominated him. Joe was his youngest child (of many) and his only son. It was not until after his father died that Joe thought of (or was able to think of) marriage. He was then 35 and Ella 25. Unlike his father Joe's eldest child was a son: the Smith (Smithson) of the tale, followed by three daughters.

That is the 'exterior' history of Rob Rider, before his return in the winter of his 'holiday year', bringing with him an apprentice of unknown origin. Of this 'boy' Rider was plainly very fond. They were on intimate and confidential terms. Rider evidently looked on him as a person of great abilities (in spite of his youth) and was confident that he would smooth over all difficulties caused by the sudden departure of the MC. It seems probable that Rider did this without warning in the expectation, or at least hope, that his apprentice would be allowed to succeed him, if the Council was faced by a sudden vacancy without time to argue or put pressure on himself. That Nokes would slip in probably never occurred to him as possible. What Alf the apprentice thought is another matter. Alf and such of Rider's previous life as can be guessed at therefore need to be examined.

It can hardly be doubted that Rider knew that Alf was an Elf in disguise. (The name Alf that he gave to him shows this, though it was sufficiently common in the village to pass without remark.) But it is also plain that he was unaware of his identity; though he supposed him to be an emissary and servant of 'The Great in Faery'; and must have known something of their purposes, being indeed himself engaged in assisting them.

Though all this is left vague in the tale, the following 'background' will serve to explain the events. The western villages of the country, among them the Woottons and Walton, were originally main points of contact between Faery and this country of Men: they had been at an earlier period actually within the Forest borders, as their names signify. Wootton Minor still remained surrounded by trees; Walton was even deeper in the Forest. The peoples of these three villages were closely related in descent; and at least in the case of the Woottons intermarriage was still frequent. Walton was however regarded now as a place where many folk were odd and oldfashioned, either because it was deeper in the Forest or simply because it was further away, seldom visited except by riders and 'travellers' from Wootton Major. (The trade routes, so to speak, of W. Major led mostly eastward.)

The crafts of Wootton, on which their present prosperity was based, actually owed their fame and commercial success in the beginning to the special skill and 'artistic' quality which contact with Faery had given to them. But the commercial success had for some time begun to have effect. The village had become comfortable and self-satisfied. The artistic quality of its products was declining, and to some extent also their traditional manual skill, though this had not yet affected their market. But the village was in a danger which it did not see: a dwindling of its prosperity, which would not be maintained for ever by 'good name' and established connexions with eastern customers, nor by mere industry and business acumen. If the thread between the villagers and Faery was broken it would go back to its squalid beginnings. All was not well indeed in the village itself. The practisers of the marketable and exportable crafts were becoming richer and more important, dominating the Council. The minor trades and professions, especially those of mere local use, were depressed; many had ceased to follow their fathers and had become hired men serving the smiths and wrights and weavers. Such folk as the Sedgers (the tale-tellers), the musicians: Pipers, Harpers, Crowthers, Fidlers and Horners* and the Sangsters, as also those skilled

> *Meaning here players on 'horns' and not workers in horn-material. These people had also the craft of making musical instruments, which had once been in some demand; though this small trade had fallen off.

in designing, painting, and in carving or smithying things of beauty. The Dyers owing to their connexion with the weaving crafts (of great importance) remained prosperous, but were (unnoticed by themselves) losing both taste and skill.

The vulgarization of Wootton is indicated by Nokes. He is obviously a somewhat extreme case, but clearly represents an attitude fast spreading in the village and growing in weight. The festivals are becoming, or have already become, mere occasions for eating and drinking. Songs, tales music dancing no longer play a part – at least they are not provided for (as is the cooking and catering) out of public funds, and if they take place at all it is in family parties, and especially in the entertainment of children. The Hall is no longer decorated, though kept in good structural order. History and legend and above all any tales touching on 'faery', have become regarded as children's stuff, patronizingly tolerated for the amusement of the very young.

This situation is evidently one that has aroused the concern of Faery. Why? It is plainly shown that Faery is a vast world in its own right, that does not depend for its existence upon Men, and which is not primarily nor indeed principally concerned with Men. The relationship must therefore be one of love: the Elven Folk, the chief and ruling inhabitants of Faery, have an ultimate kinship with Men and have a permanent love for them in general. Though they are not bound by any moral obligation to assist Men, and do not need their help (except in human affairs), they do from time to time try to assist them, avert evil from them and have relations with them, especially through certain men and women whom they find suitable.* They, the Elvenfolk are thus 'beneficent' with regard to Men,

> *It is of course possible that they <u>have a</u> 'moral' obligation (the sanctions of which we do not know). It may be contained in the word 'kinship', and also be due to the fact that in the last resort the enemy (or enemies) of Faery are the same as those of Men. Certainly the Elvish world as here depicted is not independent of the <u>existence</u> of the Human world, as distinct from Men. The world known to Men as their habitation did and could exist without Men; but not Men without it. It is probable that the world of Faery could not exist without our world, and is affected by the events in it – the reverse being also true. The 'health' of both is affected by state of the other. Men have not the power to assist the Elvenfolk in the ordering and defence of their realm; but the Elves have the power (subject to finding co-operation from within) to assist in the protection of our world, especially in the attempt to re-direct Men when their development tends to the defacing or destruction of their world. The Elves may thus have also an enlightened self-interest in human affairs.

and are not wholly alien, though many things and creatures in Faery itself are alien to Men and even actively hostile. Their good will is seen mainly in attempting to keep or restore relationships between the two worlds, since the Elves (and still some Men) realize that this love of Faery is essential to the full and proper human development. The love of Faery is the love of love: a relationship towards all things, animate and inanimate, which includes love and respect, and removes or modifies the spirit of possession and domination. Without it even plain 'Utility' will in fact become less useful; or will turn to ruthlessness and lead only to mere power, ultimately destructive.* The Apprentice relationship in the tale is thus interesting. Men in a large part of their activities are or should be in an apprentice status as regards the Elven folk. In an attempt to rescue Wootton from

> *For this reason the Elvenfolk are chary of giving to any human person possession of any device of their own which is endowed with Elvish power called by Men by many names, such as <u>magic</u>. Most Men will certainly misuse it as a mere instrument for their own personal power and success. All men will tend to cling to it as a personal possession.

its decline, the Elves reverse the situation, and the King of Faery himself comes and serves as an apprentice in the village.

This was arranged through Rider. In his youthful journeys Rider was attracted by the Forest. At some time, probably about the time when he became eighteen, he ventured in to it, and came by 'accident' upon one of the 'entrances' to Faery*.

> *This was probably arranged for or awaited by the Elves. They show a very considerable knowledge of the people of the villages and of their marriages and heredity. How they obtained this is not revealed; but the events of the tale show that it would have been possible for Elves in disguise to go about the villages unrecognized – especially as 'riders' and 'travellers' and itinerant workfolk. That a Rider was picked out for a special contact is thus understandable. Many of the associates of young Rob Rider in his early wanderings about the country may have been in fact Elvish, by whose society and talk he was guided in the desired directions and frame of mind.

Of his adventures there we do not know anything. They occurred evidently between his eighteenth and thirty-fifth year. That they were like those reported of the Smith is probable, but they would not be the same. For one thing it seems clear that he never <u>saw</u> either the King or the Queen, though he knew of their existence and was largely directed by their commands or requests. He probably ran into grave perils, and to these may be due both his occasional returns to Wootton (for rest) and his increasingly quiet and thoughtful manner, which was particularly noticed when at 35 he returned to Wootton with a wife and 'settled down'.

The King saw that for his missionary plan he needed men who knew far more of Faery than had been acquired by men for a very long time, but that these 'explorers' must have some protection. He therefore devised the token or insigne of the silver star, devised it or revived it. His own insigne was a brilliant star upon the forehead. The token was a very small representation of this. Those who wore it were thus accredited (as if they were stamped with a crown and OHMS!) and received the guidance and guard of all Elvenfolk, as being in the King's service or in his favour. But it remained the King's property, and was not transferable, nor heritable.*

*Neither of course did it confer on the wearer the right to do as he pleased or go where he wished in Faery.

This star was evidently given to Rider at some time during his later visits to Faery. Not directly by the King (unless in disguise), but by a messenger from the King; so that Rider knew from the outset something of its nature and purpose, and realized the greatness of the favour – and that it was sooner or later to be surrendered. It seems probable that Rider gave up visiting Faery when he fell in love with and married the beautiful Rose Sangster of Walton.* He returned to Wootton.

> *Heredity plays a great part in the tale. Thus Rider's mother was a Piper of Wootton Minor; his wife was one of the Sangsters of the still more 'oldfashioned' Walton, where Elvish traditions (and contacts) were still maintained. Through his daughter Ella these crafts became united with the great craft of the Smith.

But disaster overtook him in the death of his wife, and in the following year he returned frequently but secretly to Faery, though he may have gone no further than its borders. As Apprentice to the MC he would still have opportunity for unnoticed brief visits. But when he was 44 and became MC himself his visits would almost certainly cease. The Master Cook was too much under observation (and for nine months or more of the year too busy) to be long away. He might of course have made the excuse of visiting his wife's kin in Walton to be away at times; but we do not hear of this. His sadness and 'air of having his mind elsewhere' was due no doubt not only to his bereavement but also to this deprivation. Suddenly he could bear it no longer and he went off on his unexpected and unprecedented holiday.

He did not say where he was going. He probably went back to Walton and there re-entered Faery at the point where he had first done this. (It is probable too that this place was also connected with Rose. She was maybe also one who visited 'Outer Faery', and it was within the bounds of Faery that he had first met her.)

During this visit he evidently made contact again with the Elven folk. And the Apprentice-plan was suggested to him. It seems likely that this occurred in a way similar to that in which the King (as Alf) later accosted the Smith. An Elvish man met him as he was leaving Faery, and claiming the authority of the King, said that he was to be taken back as Rider's Apprentice. Rider agreed. Of course during his journey back to Wootton, and still more during his three years' close association with 'Alf' Rider would learn much concerning the King's project. He did not guess that Alf was the King but accepted him as an Elf with the authority of the King. In private he treated him as an equal or superior. No doubt it was at first rather to his surprise, even dismay, when Alf insisted on appearing in Wootton as a young boy.* But this he explained as necessary. It was easier to pass himself off

*Since evidently Rider did not intend to return to the office of MC, of which he was weary, for longer

than was necessary to establish his apprentice, the apparent extreme youth of Alf was likely to present difficulties. The Council had, it appears, no right to interfere in the choice of apprentice, and that included a reasonable expectation of succession. Though appointment as MC was nominally made by the Council, they did not as a rule interfere; but they had the right to do so, especially in the absence of the MC (sc. if he died in office, or as in this case without precedent left the village). Rider had been just, and (as he thought) politic in praising Alf's skill and general competence, but the Council contrary to his hope now exercised their right when faced by what seemed to them the absurdity of appointing to a major office a person who appeared to be a rather tall lad but not much more than fifteen years old.

as a 'boy'. Also he intended to make a very long stay in Wootton – including in his plans the making of at least two Great Cakes, which would be memorable, and leaving behind a tradition of a long 'reign' of light colour and mirth, as well as culinary excellence, together with the rumour that this was due to a beneficent intrusion from Faery. It was therefore necessary to allow time for him to appear to age in human fashion at an at least credible rate.

Alf himself must have been well aware that the situation and mood of the village (which he had come to cure) would effectively prevent his appointment when Rider went off, and was content with remaining apprentice. This he would of course do.

An incoming MC in such a situation could not even if he wished dismiss the properly appointed apprentice, at the least until he had been some years in office, and even then he would have to make good charges of incompetence. It may be surmised that the appointment of Nokes was in fact part of Alf's plan, and 'arranged' by him – in the three years he had made 'friends' in the village and no doubt found it easy to spread an opinion that Nokes should be given a chance. This was, as it were, a direct attack on the core of the vulgarity and smugness in Wootton, possibly with some (if not much) hope of a conversion. Nokes however proved too vain and also too ungenerous a character. He was shrewd or sly enough to recognize Alf's usefulness to himself, but Alf's courtesy only increased Nokes' domineering manner, while his services produced not gratitude but dislike. Nokes had however a virtue, or the remains of one. He seems to have been generally fond of children, in his way: a facetious and patronizing way; yet it allowed him to

SMITH OF WOOTTON MAJOR

admit 'Fairy' at least as a thing to* amuse them, and he enjoyed the fun of the 'lucky bits' in the Cake. Of this Alf made

> *It seems probable that the notion of the 'Fairy Queen' on the Cake was indeed Nokes' own, though he was too lazy to carry it out himself. It will be noted that Alf carries out Nokes' notion, only mitigating it by skill and beauty in its own way. He even included the silly notion that 'fairies' must have 'magic wands', that was one of Nokes' fixed ideas. It was of course an insult to the Queen, and nevertheless a 'glimpse' of Faery for the receptive. As the Queen later explains.

good use. Alf was as generous as Nokes was ungenerous; and he seems to have had a kind feeling (not solely one of pity) for Nokes: probably based on his kindness to children (according to his lights), not only at the one entertainment for them of which the tale gives an account. His last conversation with Nokes as a very old man must not be taken as baiting or gloating over a stupid and defeated opponent. It was an attempt (if desperate) to come to terms before Alf departed, and get into the old man's head some dim glimpse of what was going on: it was probably intended to lead finally to a hint that the honour of the star was going to fall to one of Nokes' own descendants. But

Nokes' outrageous rudeness – after all, Faery apart, he was talking to a man who had been MC longer than he had – was too great to be endured. Alf showed pity and kindness in return for the confession (even though it was made only in fear) that Nokes was 'only a poor old man'; and more subtly, by arranging that Nokes' injured pride could take refuge in the idea that it was only a dream.

A few points remain. How did Alf come to be accepted? Why was Rider more merry after he returned from his holiday? Where did he go after his final departure?

Alf was probably introduced in Wootton Major by Rider as 'Alf from Walton'. His youth would explain his having no craft name. There remained a tradition that Walton folk were 'kinsmen', though now oldfashioned and very seldom visited, and this would fit the situation. A young fellow from one of the more eastern villages might have been resented, but also expected to be more normal. Rider's wife was known to have come from Walton; and many no doubt assumed that Alf was some one from among her kin.

Rider was more merry, because he thought he had found a solution of his own difficulty. He was in touch with Faery during the black year after his young wife's death; and offering himself to the MC and so becoming himself MC in due course was no doubt urged on him by the King (through emissaries). He did his best – which was very good – but he soon became very tired of the office and its publicity and restriction on his movements. After 18 years he could stand it no longer without a break. But the 'apprentice plan' gave him a hope of leaving the office without any real harm to the village, while furthering the King's designs. Also he was refreshed by his visit to Faery.

He stayed the minimum time in office, and then went away – no doubt back to Walton. He clearly thought it likely that he would see Alf again, and before so very long, since he was himself already 65. This meeting he must have expected to be within the borders of Faery. Rider was now 'unstarred', but he must have planned to visit at least Outer Faery. His daughter was now happily married and busy, and he felt free. He went back to Walton, where by the 'entrance' long familiar to him, he could enter Faery, but live and end his days among his wife's kin. It will be noted that the smith when in his turn 'unstarred' did not intend ever to revisit Faery. Doubtless he could have done so, had he wished. But he could not have gone deep into the realm again. His experiences had plainly been far more perilous and exalted than Rider's, and he was no longer able to rest content with 'Outer Faery'. He must either abstain or be tempted to go on journeys for which he no longer had 'licence' or protection. And he was not free. He had his family to consider. Especially his son. He had ten or even fifteen good years work still in him, and must set his son up as fully as possible in his craft before he retired. His son was already twenty-four and not yet married. While Nell and his daughter Nan were probably themselves elf-friends and even walkers in Outer Faery, Ned was dependent on his father: he could receive 'Faery' only through the lore and companionship of the older Smith. He was thus one precisely of the practical and plain normal men and workers whose enlightenment and vivification was one of the objects of the King's plan.

There is no need to hunt for allegory. Such teaching as this slender story contains is implicit, and would be no less present if it were a plain narrative of historical events. But (as in my stories generally) it will be observed that there is no religion. There is no church or temple. Among the professions there is no parson or priest. The festivals are the nearest approach. To judge by the only one named, the Winter Feast at midwinter, they must have been seasonal: associated with Spring and Midsummer and Harvest and the like. In origin such festivals are not separable from 'religion', but in Wootton Major at the time of the tale they have evidently no longer any religious reference: no more than our surviving Quarter Days as such. (No power or powers are by any ceremony propitiated, supplicated or thanked.) In a story written by a religious man this is a plain indication that religion is not absent but subsumed: the tale is not about religion or in particular about its relation to other things. It does not therefore appear <u>as such</u>. Otherwise a short essay on its point would have been better than a tale.

The Great Hall is evidently in a way an 'allegory' of the village church; the Master Cook with his house adjacent, and his office that is not hereditary, provides for its own instruction and succession but is not one of the 'secular' or profitable crafts, and yet is supported financially by the village, is plainly the Parson and the priesthood. 'Cooking' is a domestic affair practised by men and women: personal religion and prayer. The Master Cook presides over and provides for all the religious festivals of the year, and also for all the religious occasions that are not universal: births, marriages, and deaths. The Great Hall is however no longer painted or decorated. If antique carvings, whether grotesques like gargoyles, or beautiful and of religious import, are preserved at all it is by mere custom. The Hall is kept rainproof, weatherproof and warm: that is the prime object of any care spent on it. Festivals are mere public assemblies, for talk assisted by eating and drinking: there are no longer songs, music, or dances. The church has been 'reformed'. Memory survives of 'merrier' days, but most of the village would not approve of any revival of them. That a MC should himself sing is regarded as out of accord with his office.

Industry and sober hard work are mainly to be commended; but the profit motive for such assiduity is becoming dominant. The less commercially profitable an occupation the less it is esteemed. (One feels that though there is yet no hint of this, the time is not far distant when the office of MC will be abolished. The Hall will become a mere place of business, the property of the Craft Council, hirable by those who can afford it for great family occasions. If any Cooks survive they will become traders, opening cookshops and eating houses adapted to the various tastes of clients.)

BUT Faery is _not_ religious. It is fairly evident that it is not Heaven or Paradise. Certainly its inhabitants,

Elves, are not Angels or emissaries of God (direct). The tale does not deal with religion itself. The Elves are not busy with a plan to reawake religious devotion in Wootton. The Cooking allegory would not be suitable to any such import. Faery represents at its weakest a breaking out (at least in mind) from the iron ring of the familiar, still more from the adamantine ring of belief that it is known, possessed, controlled, and so (ultimately) all that is worth being considered – a constant awareness of a world beyond these rings. More strongly it represents love: that is, a love and respect for all things, 'inanimate' and 'animate', an unpossessive love of them as 'other'. This 'love' will produce both <u>ruth</u> and <u>delight</u>. Things seen in its light will be respected, and they will also appear delightful, beautiful, wonderful even glorious. Faery might be said indeed to represent Imagination (without definition because taking in all the definitions of this word): esthetic: exploratory and receptive; and artistic: inventive, dynamic, (sub)creative. This compound – of awareness of a limitless world outside our domestic parish; a love (in ruth and admiration) for the things in it; and a desire for wonder, marvels, both perceived and conceived – this 'Faery' is as necessary for the health and complete functioning of the Human as is sunlight for physical life: sunlight as distinguished from the soil, say, though it in fact permeates and modifies even that.

There was a village once, not very long ago for those with long memories, nor very far away for those with long legs. It was not very large, but a fair number of folk lived in it, good bad and mixed, as is usual, and some were a bit elvish, as was at that time also common enough. It was not a very remarkable village, except in one thing. It had a large Cook-house, and the Master Cook was an important person; for the Cook-house was part of the Village-hall: the largest and oldest building in the place, and the only one that was really beautiful. In it once a week the vilagers had a meal together, and most of them came regularly, except the very old, or the very young, or any that might be ill. Also there were various festivals during the year, for which the Cook had to prepare special feasts.

There was one festival to which all looked forward, even the very old, for it was the only one in the winter. It lasted several days, and on the last day at sundown there was an entertainment for children, which they called a Party ; meaning that only a part of the village children came to it (by invitation). There were never more than twenty four invitations and it was an honour to get one. I daresay that some who deserved one were left out, and some who did not were invited by mistake, for that is the way of things, however careful those who arrange such maters may try to be. Anyway it was sheer luck (as we say) if you happened to come in for a Great Party; for that was only provided once in twenty four years, and the Cook was supposed to do his very best for the occasion. Among many other delicious things which children especially liked (in his opinion), he usually provided a Great Cake ; and by the success of that he was usually remembered, for no Cook ever had a chance of making

[Hybrid draft and transcription of 'The Great Cake']

There was a village once, not very long ago for those with long memories, nor very far away for those with long legs. It was large, and a fair number of folk lived in it, good bad and mixed, as is usual, and some were a bit elvish, as was at that time still common though people of that land were not well thought-of. It was not a very remarkable village, except in one thing. It had a large Cook-house, and the Master Cook was an important person; for the Cook-house was part of the Village-Hall: the largest and oldest building in the place, and the only one that was really beautiful. In it once a week the villagers had a meal together, and most of them came regularly, except the very old, or the very young, or any that might be ill. Also there were various festivals during the year, for which the Cook had to prepare special feasts.

There was one festival to which all looked forward, even the very old, for it was the only one in the winter. It lasted several days, and on the last day at sundown there was an entertainment for children, which they called a Party; meaning that only a part of the village children came to it (by invitation). There were never more than twenty four invitations and it was an honour to get one. I daresay that some who deserved one were left out, and some who did not were invited by mistake, for that is the way of things, however careful those who arrange such matters may try to be. Anyway it was sheer luck (as we say) if you happened to come in for a Great Party; for that was only provided once in twenty four years, and the Cook was supposed to do his very best for the occasion. Among many other delicious things which children especially liked (in his opinion), he usually provided a Great Cake; and by the success of that

his name was remembered afterwards, for the Master Cooks seldom lived long
enough to make more than one Great Cake.

There came a time, however, when the Master Cook reigning to everyone's
surprise, for it
had never happened before, said that he wanted a holiday; and he went away,
no one knew where, and when he came back he seemed raher changed. His cooking
if anything was changed for the better, though some of his dishes and sweetmeats were new, and being unfamiliar were not to everyone's taste. He had
been a rather serious man who said very little, but now he was often
joking, saying and doing quite ridiculous things, and at feasts he would
insist on singing songs, which was not expected of Master Cooks. Also he
brought with him an Apprentice; and that was astonishing.

It was not astonishing for the Master Cook to have an Apprentice. It was
usual. The Master Cook chose one, and taught him all that he could; and as
they both grew older no doubt the Apprentice did most of the
work, so that when the Master died or retired, there he was, ready to take
over and become the Master Cook in his turn. But this Master had never chosen
an Apprentice. He had always said 'Time enough yet'; or, 'I'm keeping my
eyes open, and I'll choose one when I find one to suit me'. But now he
brought with him a mere boy, and not one from the village. He was lighter-
built than most of the villagers, and quicker, soft-spoken and very polite; but ridiculously young for the job. Still choosing his apprentice was the Master Cook's
affair, and no one had any right to interfere in it; so the boy was let be, and
soon folk became to be used to seeing him about, and he made some friends.

The next surprise came only a year or two later. One spring morning
the Master Cook took off his tall white hat, folded up his clean aprons,
hung up his white coat, took a stout ash stick and a small bag

'THE GREAT CAKE'

his name was remembered afterwards, for the Master Cooks seldom lived long enough to make more than one Great Cake.

There came a time, however, when the reigning Master Cook to everyone's surprise, for it had never happened before, said that he wanted a holiday; and he went away, no one knew where, and when he came back he seemed rather changed. His cooking if anything was changed for the better, though some of his dishes and sweetmeats were new, and being unfamiliar were not to everyone's taste. He had been a rather serious man who said very little, but now he was often joking, saying and doing quite ridiculous things, and at feasts he would insist on singing songs, which was not expected of Master Cooks. Also he brought with him an Apprentice; and that was astonishing.

It was not astonishing for the Master Cook to have an apprentice. It was usual. The Master Cook chose one, more often than not one of his own sons, and taught him all that he could; and as they both grew older no doubt the apprentice did most of the work, so that when the Master died or retired, there he was, ready to take over and become the Master Cook in his turn. But this Master had no son and had never chosen an apprentice. He had always said 'Time enough yet'; or 'I'm keeping my eyes open, and I'll choose one when I find one to suit me'. But now he brought with him a mere boy, and not one from the village. He was lighter-built than most of the villagers, and quicker, soft-spoken and very polite; but ridiculously young for the job, hardly in his teens by the look of him. Still choosing his apprentice was the Master Cook's affair, and no one had any right to interfere in it; so the boy was let be, and soon folk became used to seeing him about, and he made some friends. Prentice most people called him, but the Cook called him Alf.

The next surprise came only three years later. One spring morning the Master Cook took off his tall white hat, folded up his clean aprons, hung up his white coat, took a stout ash stick and a small bag, and said good-bye to the Apprentice; no one else was about. 'Good-bye for now, Edwy,' he said. 'I leave you to manage things as well as you can. I hope things go well. If we meet again, I expect to hear all about it. Tell them that I've gone on another holiday, a long one I hope; and that when that's over I shan't be coming back'.

There was quite a stir in the village when the Apprentice gave this message to people that came to the Cook-house . 'What a thing to do!' they said. 'And he's never made a Great Cake; it's still four years to the next. And what are we to do without any Master Cook?' But in all the arguments and discussions that followed nobody ever thought of making the young Apprentice into the Cook. He had grown a bit taller, but still looked like a boy, and he had only served for three years. In the end for lack of any better they appointed a man of the village, who had a good name as a cook in a private way, though he was not much of a baker. He was a solid sort of man with a wife and children, and careful of money. 'At any rate he won't go off without notice' they said; 'and even a poor dinner is better than none'.

Nokes, for that was his name, was very pleased with the turn things had taken. For some time he used to put on the tall white hat when he was alone in the kitchen and look at himself in a polished frying pan (there were no mirrors in the village) and say; 'Good morning, Master! That hat suits you properly, makes you look quite tall. I hope things go well with you'.

They went well enough; for Nokes, indeed a respectable Cook, and he had the Apprentice But in due course the time for the Great Party began to draw near, and Nokes had to think about making the Cake. It worried him a bit, for although with years' practice he could turn out

'THE GREAT CAKE'

and said goodbye to Prentice; no one else was about. 'Good-bye for now, Alf,' he said. 'I leave you to manage things as well as you can. I hope things go well. If we meet again, I expect to hear all about it. Tell them that I've gone on another holiday, a long one, I hope; and that when that's over I shan't be coming back'.

There was quite a stir in the village when Prentice gave this message to people that came to the Cook-house. 'What a thing to do [without warning or farewell]!' they said. 'And what are we to do without any Master Cook? He has left no one to take his place.' For in all the arguments and discussions nobody ever thought of making young Prentice into the Cook. He had grown a bit taller, but still looked like a boy, and he had only served for three years. In the end for lack of any better they appointed a man of the village, who was a good enough cook in a small way, though he was not much of a baker. [When he was younger he had helped the Master now and again, but the Master had not taken to him, and never made him his apprentice.] He was a solid sort of man with a wife and children, and careful of money. 'At any rate he won't go off without notice' they said; 'and even poor cooking is better than none.' And some added: 'It is seven years to the next Great Cake; he may be good enough by then.' Nokes, for that was his name, was very pleased with the turn things had taken. For some time he used to put on the tall white hat when he was alone in the kitchen and look at himself in a polished frying pan and say; 'Good morning, Master! That hat suits you properly, makes you look quite tall. I hope things go well with you'. They went well enough, for Nokes did his best and he had the Apprentice to help him, and indeed to teach him, though that Nokes never admitted. But in due course the time for the Great Party began to draw near, and Nokes had to think about making the Great Cake. Secretly he was worried about it, for although with seven years' practice he could turn out

[The two succeeding pages are missing, and the narrative resumes in mid-sentence at the top of page six with a remark by the Cook.]

◂◂ 151 ▸▸

'Very pretty and fairylike he siad, though he hadno idea what that meant, his plan
for/~~hismtush~~ was to stick a little doll on top, dressed in cotton-wool,
with a little wand in her hand ending a tinsel star.   But before he set
to work, having only dim memories of what should go inside a 'party cake',
he looked in some old books of recipes. They puzzled him, for they mentioned
many things that he had not heard of, or had forgotten, and did not know
of these
where to find. Some/he thought very unsuitable, since they were not sweet
at all, nor very soft; but he thought he might try some of the spices that
the books spoke of. He scratched his head and remembered and old black,
box with different compartments in which the cook whose place he had taken hadonce kept
spices, and other things for special cakes. It was on a high shelf and he
had not looked inside for a long time.
                                                                    was
When he got it down, he found that very lttle of the spices ~~were~~ left,
and what there was was rather dry and musty; but in one compartment he found
a ring, black-lookingas if it was made of silver and was tarnished. 'That's
funny!' he said, as he held it up to the light.   'No, it isn't!' said a
                                                                    who
voice that made him jump ; for it was the voice of his apprentice ~~that~~ had
come in behind him, and ~~hadnetwithout~~ he had never yet
dared to speak first before he was spoken to. He was only a small boy;
bright and quick, 'but he has a lot to learn yet' (so the cook thought).
So 'What do you mean, my lad'.said the cook, not much pleased. 'If it
isn't funny; what is it?'   'It's a magic ring', said the apprentice.
Then the cook laughed. 'All right, all right', he said. 'Call it what you
like! You'll grow up someday. Now you can get on with stoning the raisins;
and if you notice any magic ones tell me.'
'What are you going to do with the ring?' said the apprentice. 'Put it
                                                                 children
in the cake, of course,' said the cook. Surely you have been to parties

'THE GREAT CAKE'

"Very pretty and fairylike' he said, though he had no idea what that meant, for his plan was to stick a little doll on top, dressed in cottonwool, with a little wand in her hand ending [in] a tinsel star. But before he set to work, having only dim memories of what should go inside a 'party cake', he looked in some old books of recipes left behind by previous cooks. They puzzled him, for they mentioned many things that he had not heard of, or had forgotten, and did not know where to find. Some of these he thought very unsuitable, since they were not sweet at all, nor very soft; but he thought he might try some of the spices that the books spoke of. He scratched his head and remembered an old black box with different compartments in which the cook whose place he had taken had once kept spices, and other things for special cakes. It was on a high shelf and he had not looked inside for a long time.

When he got it down, he found that very little of the spices was left, and that was rather dry and musty, but in one compartment he found a ring, black-looking as if it was made of silver and was tarnished. 'That's funny!' he said, as he held it up to the light. 'NO, it isn't!' said a voice that made him jump; for it was the voice of his apprentice who had come in behind him, and he had never yet dared to speak first before he was spoken to. He was only a small boy; bright and quick, 'but he has a lot to learn yet' (so the cook thought).

So 'What do you mean, my lad' said the cook, not much pleased. 'If it isn't funny, what is it?' 'It's a magic ring' said the apprentice. Then the cook laughed. 'All right, all right,' he said. 'Call it what you like! You'll grow up someday. Now you can get on with stoning the raisins; and if you notice any magic ones tell me'.

'What are you going to do with the ring?' said the apprentice. 'Put it in the cake, of course,' said the cook. 'Surely you have been to children's parties yourself, and not so long ago, where little trinkets like this were stirred into the mixture, and little silver coins and what not: it amuses the children, Cook?' 'But this is not a trinket, it's a magic ring' said the apprentice 'so you've said before said the Cook crossly. Very well, I'll tell the children. It'll make them laugh.'

In time the cake was made and iced and decorated, and stood in the middle of the tea-table, lit with red candles all round it, and the children looked at it; and some said 'Isn't it pretty and fairylike!': which pleased the Cook, but not the apprentice. (They were both there, the cook to cut the cake when the time came, and the apprentice to hand him the knife which he had sharpened)

At last the Cook took the knife and stepped up to the table. 'I should tell you my dears' he said, 'that inside this lovely icing there is cake made of many nice things to eat, but also stirred well in there is a number of pretty little things, trinkets and little coins and what not; and I am told that it is lucky to find one of them in your slice. And there is also tonight a ring, a magic ring (or so my boyhere says). So be careful. If you break one of your pretty front teeth on it, the magic ring won't mend it. It won't, willit, my lad?' he said turning to the apprentice; but they boy did not answer.

It was quite a good cake; and when it was all cutup there was a slice for everyone of the children and nothing left over. The slices soon disappeared, and every now and again a trinket or a coin was discovered; some found one, and some found two, and several found none, for that is the way luck goes. But when it was all eaten, there was no sign of any magic ring.

'Bless me!' said the Cook. 'It must have been magical . Unless it was not made of silver after all, and has melted; and that's more likely'. He looked at the apprentice with a smile; and the apprentice looked at him and did not smile.

But the ring was magical (the apprentice was the kind of person who

'THE GREAT CAKE'

yourself, and not so long ago, where little trinkets like this were stirred into the mixture, and little silver coins and what not: it amuses the children.' 'But Cook? this is not a trinket, it's a magic ring' said the apprentice. 'So you've said before' said the Cook crossly. 'Very well, I'll tell the children. It'll make them laugh.'

In time the cake was made and iced and decorated acc[ording] to the Cook's fancy. At the Party it stood in the middle of the tea-table inside a ring of 24 small red candles, and the children looked at it with wide eyes; and some said 'Isn't it pretty and fairylike!': which pleased the Cook, but not the apprentice. (They were both there, the cook to cut the cake when the time came, and the apprentice to hand him the knife which he had sharpened.)

At last the Cook took the knife and stepped up to the table. 'I should tell you my dears' he said, 'that inside this lovely icing there is a cake made of many nice things to eat, but also stirred well in there is a number of pretty little things, trinkets and little coins and what not; and I am told that it is lucky to find one of them in your slice. And there is also tonight a ring, a magic ring (or so my boy here says). So be careful. If you break one of your pretty front teeth on it, the magic ring won't mend it. It won't, will it, my lad?' he said turning to the apprentice; but the boy did not answer.

It was quite a good cake; and when it was all cut up there was a slice for everyone of the children and nothing left over. The slices soon disappeared, and every now and again a trinket or a coin was discovered; some found one, and some found two, and several found none, for that is the way luck goes. But when it was all eaten, there was no sign of any magic ring.

'Bless me!' said the Cook. 'It must have been magical. Unless it was not made of silver after all, and has melted; and that's more likely.' He looked at the apprentice with a smile; and the apprentice looked at him and did not smile.

But the ring was magical (the apprentice was the kind of person who about the up

who did not make mistakes /of that sort); and what had happened was thhat one of the children (almost boy?) had swallowed it without ever notiwing it. And he (or she (I do not remember which it was, and of course it does not matter) did not notice it for a long time after, not till the cake and the party had been forgotten by all the others who were there; but the ring remainde with him, tucked in some place where it could not be felt (for it was made to do so), until the day came. The party had been in winter, but it was now early summer, and the night was hardly dark at all. The boy got up before dawn, for he ~~fahbmmsuhimsm~~ did not wish to sleep. He looked out of thhe window, and the world seemed quiet and expectant. Then the dawn came, and far away he heard the dawn-song of the birds beginning, and coming towards him, until ~~hm~~ it rushed over him, filling all the land round his house, and passed on like a wave of music into the West; and the sun rose over the trees.

It reminds me of Fairy' he heard himself say; 'but in Fairy the people sing too'. And he began to sing in strange words; and in that moment the ring fell out of his mouth, and he caught it. It was bright silver now, glittering in the sun, and he put it on the forefinger of his right hand, and it fitted, and he wore it for many years. Few people noticed it, though it was not invisible; but very few could help noticing his eyes and his voice. His eyes had a light in them; and his voice which had begun to grwo beautiful as soon as the ring came to him,

'THE GREAT CAKE'

who did not make mistakes about things of that sort); and what had happened was that one of the small boys had swallowed it without ever noticing it. And he did not notice it for a long time after, not till the Cake and the Party had been almost forgotten by the other children who were there; but the ring remained with the boy, tucked in some place where it could not be felt (for it was made to do so), until its day came.

The party had been in winter, but it was now early summer, and the night was hardly dark at all. The boy got up before dawn, for he did not wish to sleep. He looked out of the window, and the world seemed quiet and expectant. Then the dawn came, and far away he heard the dawn-song of the birds beginning, and coming towards him, until it rushed over him, filling all the land round his house, and passed on like a wave of music into the West; and the sun rose over the trees.

'It reminds me of Fairy' he heard himself say; 'but in Fairy the people sing too'. And he began to sing in strange words; and in that moment the ring fell out of his mouth, and he caught it. It was bright silver now, glittering in the sun, and he put it on the forefinger of his right hand, and it fitted, and he wore it for many years. Few people noticed it, though it was not invisible; but very few could help noticing his eyes and his voice. His eyes had a light in them; and his voice which had begun to grow beautiful as soon as the ring came to him,

[Here the typescript. breaks off in mid-page. The story continues in a careful manuscript hand on small, lined notebook or writing-pad paper, hand-marked in the upper right-hand corner 'a' through 'h'.]

became ever more beautiful as he grew up. He became well-known in the neighbourhood for his good workmanship. His father was a smith, and he followed his trade; and bettered it. He made many useful things — pots and pans, bars and bolts, and hinges and horseshoes, and the like — and they were good and strong, and also they had a grace about them, being shapely in their kinds; and some things he made for delight that were beautiful, for he could work iron into wonderful forms and designs, that seemed as light and delicate as a spray of leaves and blossom, but kept the stern strength of iron. Few could pass by one of his gates or lattices without stopping to admire it; none could pass through it once it was shut. Often he sang as he worked. And not till then most people knew about him — it was enough indeed and more than most men achieve. But (indeed) he also became well acquainted with

'THE GREAT CAKE'

became ever more beautiful as he grew up. He became well-known in the neighbourhood for his good workmanship. His father was a smith, and he followed his trade; and bettered it. He made many useful things – tools, and pans, and bars and bolts, and hinges and horseshoes, and the like – and they were good and strong, and also they had a grace about them, being shapely in their kind; and some things he made for delight that were beautiful, for he could work iron into wonderful forms and designs, that seemed as light and delicate as a spray of leaves and blossom, but kept the stern strength of iron or seemed even stronger. Few could pass by one of his gates or lattices without stopping to admire it: none could pass through it once it was shut. Often he sang as he worked. And that was all that most people knew about him – it was enough indeed and more than most men achieve. But he also became acquainted with

Faery, and loved some part of it well as well as any
mortal can, though, except for his wife and one of
his children, few ever opened their hearts about it.
But he was welcome in Faery, and seldom in danger
there; for the evil things avoided the star.

One day, however, he was walking through a
wood in Faery, and it was autumn there, and there were
red leaves on the branches, and upon the ground. Footsteps
came behind, but he was thinking about the leaves,
and did not turn round. A man caught up with
him, and said suddenly at his side:
"Are you going my way, Gilthir?" That
was his name (Starbrow) in Faery; at home he was
called Alfred Smithson. "What is your way?"
he answered. "I am going home now." said the
man, and Alfred looked at him and saw that it
was the Apprentice: a tall man now, but he stooped
a little, and had lines on his tired face, though he was
only a few years older than Alfred. "So am I,"
he said, "we will walk together".

They went on side by side in silence for many
miles in silence, except for the rustle of red leaves

'THE GREAT CAKE'

Fairy, and knew some parts of it well – as well as any mortal can, though, except for his wife and one of his children, few ever guessed it. But he was welcome in Fairy, and seldom in danger there: for the evil things avoided the star.

One day, however, he was walking through a wood in Fairy, and it was autumn there, and there were red leaves but not on the boughs and on the ground. Footsteps came behind, but he was thinking about the leaves, and did not turn round. A man caught up with him, and said suddenly at his side: "Are you going my way, Gilthir?" For that was his name (Starbrow) in Fairy; at home he was called Alfred Smithson. "What is your way?" he answered. "I am going home", said the man, and Alfred looked at him and saw that it was the Apprentice: a tall man now, but he stooped a little, and had lines on his brow and face, though he was only a few years older than Alfred. "So am I," he said; "Come: we will walk together."

They went on side by side for many miles in silence, except for the rustle of red leaves at their feet. But at length, before they left Faery, the Apprentice stopped, and turning to Alfred, touched him star. "Don't you think you gave this thing up?" he said.

"Why should I? Isn't it mine? It came to me after a gift."

"Why? Because one should not cling too long to such gifts. They can't belong to one for ever. And because it is time now for it to have another owner. Someone else needs it."

"Then what should I do? Give it to some one who lives in Faery? Great Ones in Faery? Which fairy?"

"You could give it me," said the Apprentice. "But you might find that too difficult. Will you come with me to my workplace and put it back in the box where your grandfather kept it?"

"I did not know that," said Alfred.

"Well, he was your mother's father, and he was the Cook before the Cook who made the cake for your party. He was the best they could find to follow your grandfather, since he had no son, and his daughter was a needlewoman. But I am Cook now. Some day soon I shall make another great party cake; and I think the star should go into it."

'THE GREAT CAKE'

at their feet. But at length, before they left Fairy, the Apprentice stopped, and turning to Alfred, touched his star. "Don't you think it is time that you gave this thing up?" he said.

"Why should I? Isn't it mine? It came in my slice of cake."

"Why? Because one should not cling too long to such gifts. They can't belong to one for ever. And because it is time now for some one new to have a turn. Some one needs it."

"Then what should I do? Give it to one of the Great Ones in Fairy? To the King perhaps."

"You could give it to me" said the Apprentice. "But you might find that too difficult. Will you come with me to my workplace and put it back in the box where your grandfather kept it?"

"I did not know that", said Alfred.

"Well, he was your mother's father, and went away before your time had come, and he was the Cook before the Cook who made the cake for your party: the best they could find to follow your grandfather, who had no son, and his daughter was a needle-woman. But I am Cook now. Some day soon I shall make another great party cake; and I think the star should go into it."

and half put the look into his breast-shelf of Strange; he
showed it to Alfred. Perhaps [...] guess [...] how [...]
people but tomorrow [...] his own Cook', I couldn't say
aloud,' he said. 'You must put the far-star to its [...] and
when [...] is to show [...] which [...]

"Very well" said Alfred. "Do you know who will
find it? I should like to know. That seemed such
a easier to part with it."

"Maybe I guess", said the Apprentice, "but the
Cook does not do the choosing. [The star, as I know
she made it, do that, I think]."

So they went back together to their village,
and Alfred put the star into a box. It was a box
now, and was filled each [...] one little compartment
and into that the star dropped and went dark.

Alfred had felt a smart as he took it from
his forehead; and he felt grieved as he let it
fall from his hand, for he thought he was
giving up his power to enter Fairy again.
But he found that it was not so. All the people
and creatures in Fairy could still see the mark
of the Star on his brows, and its light was still in
his eyes. But [...] ever after that he never
saw any new things in Fairy, nor came into
regions that he had not visited before.

'THE GREAT CAKE'

[addition in rough script at top of page:
and the Apprentice took the box from its shelf in the storeroom. He showed it to Alfred. Perhaps it was the spices, which were fresh and pungent, but his eyes watered. I can't see very clearly,' he said. You must put it in for me. So he gave it to the Apprentice and the star dropped into its place and went dark.]

"Very well" said Alfred. "Do you know who will find it? I should like to know. That would make it easier to part with it."

"Maybe I guess", said the Apprentice; "but the Cook does not do the choosing. [The star, or those who made it, do that, I think].

So they went back together to their village and Alfred put the star into the box. It was clean now, and well filled except for one little compartment that was empty, and into that the star dropped and went dark.

Alfred had felt a smart as he took it from his forehead; and he felt grieved now as he let [heard] it fall [into the box] from his hand, for he thought he was giving up his power ever to enter Fairy again. But he found that it was not so. All the people and creatures in Fairy could still see the mark of the star on his brow, and its light remained in his eyes. But after that he never saw any new things in Fairy, nor came into regions that he had not visited before.

Now it is (perhaps) a strange thing, but the old Cook, who had laughed at the Apprentice, had never been able to put out of his mind that cake or the Star, although he had gone on being Cook for many years. He was an old man now, and cooked toe tonight. He was very fat, for he went on eating though and was fond of sugar. Most of his days he spent sitting in a big chair by his window, or at his door if it was fine. He liked talking, since he had many opinions to share, and to air; and he was always glad if any one would stop and speak (or listen) to him.

The Apprentice often did — so the old Cook still called him, and expected himself to be called Master by him. That the Apprentice never failed to do, which was a great point in his favour, though there were many others the old Cook found him thoughtless intolerable though there were others the old Cook liked better. One day he was nodding in his chair, when he found the Apprentice standing by, looking down at him. "Good evening!" said he, said the old man. "I am glad to see you, for I have a thing on my mind, nothing of sleeping, that you may remember. I shall wonder so at that little Star I do : the one that years ago I put in the best cake I ever made (and that's saying something). But

'THE GREAT CAKE'

Now it is (perhaps) a strange thing, but the old Cook, who had laughed at the Apprentice, had never been able to put out of his mind that cake or the star, although he had gone on being Cook for many years. He was a very old man now, and [had not] cooked no longer [for years]. He was very fat, for he went on eating heartily and he was fond of sugar. Most of his days he spent sitting in a big chair by his window, or at his door if it was fine. He liked talking, since he had many opinions to share, or to air; and he was always glad if anyone would stop and speak (or listen) to him.

The Apprentice often [sometimes] did – so the old Cook still called him, and expected himself to be called Master. That the Apprentice never [seldom] failed to do, which was a great point in his favour, though there were others the old Cook liked better.

One afternoon he was nodding in his chair after dinner, when he found the Apprentice standing by looking down at him. "Good afternoon" said the old man. "I am glad to see you, for I have a thing on my mind, waking or sleeping, that you may remember. I still wonder about that little star, I do: the one that years ago I put in the best cake I ever made (and that's saying something). But maybe you have forgotten it."

"No mother, I remember it very well. But is it troubling you? It was a good cake, and it was praised and enjoyed."

"Oh the cake was of course, I won't it. But that does not trouble me. It's the star. I cannot make up my mind what became of it — anyhow. I said it must have melted, but that was only to stop the children being frightened. Of course it wouldn't melt. Then I too have thought that some one must have swallowed it. But is it likely? You might swallow a little coin and not notice it, but not that star. It was small, but it had sharp points."

"But you don't think that it was made of — ? Don't trouble your head. Some one swallowed it, I assure you." "Can't you guess who?"

"Well I have a long memory, and not many sticks... and in cakes — and I can recall all the children's names. Let me think! Was it Nelly Bullen? She was a greedy, as bothered her friend; she is fat as a barrel now."

"Yes there are some folk who get like that," said the Apprentice, looking at the cook's outheart. "But wasn't it Nelly. She found a threepenny bit in her slice."

'THE GREAT CAKE'

maybe you have forgotten it?"

"No master, I remember it very well. But what is troubling you? It was a good cake, and it was praised and enjoyed."

"Of course. I made it. But that does not trouble me. It's the star. I cannot make up my mind what became of it. I said it must have melted, but that was only to stop the children being frightened. Of course it wouldn't melt. Then I have thought that some one must have swallowed it. But is it likely? You might swallow a little coin and not notice it, but not that star. It was small, but it had sharp points."

"But you don't know what it was made of master! Don't trouble yourself [mind]. Some one swallowed it, I assure you. Can't you guess who?"

"Well I have a long memory and that day sticks in it, and I can recall all the children's names. Let me think! Was it Molly Miller? She was a greedy and bolted her food; she is fat as a barrel [sack] now."

"Yes, there are some folk who get like that, Master" said the Apprentice, looking at the Cook's waistcoat. "But it wasn't Molly. She found a threepenny bit in her slice."

"So she did! Harry Cooper then? He has a
Crop mouth like a frog's and shuffled his cheeks."

"Oh no! He would not swallow a raisin-pip.
I left 4 or one or two in, and wished them to him. He
took them out of his mouth with his fingers."

"Then that little girl — Lily Long? — she has been
putting water. She used to swallow pins as a
baby, and came to no harm."

"Oh no! She only ate the marzipan and sugar,
and gave the inside to Teddy Fuller she sat by."

"Then I give up. Who was it? (You seem to
have been watching very carefully, and making sure.)"

"Alfred Smithson, of course, Mater," said the
Apprentice.

"Go on!" laughed the old Cook. "I ought to have
known you were having a game with me, and why
I tell up. Don't be ridiculous! Alfred Smithson
is a plain hardworking man now, as he was
a quite sensible boy then. Contrive, you might say —
thought before he spoke. Looked all round before
he jumped. He would not go swallowing anything
that might do him harm. Chewed before he swallowed
— and still does, if you take my meaning."

"I do, Mater. But very interesting — the star at
the bone. You must think what you think. But
the star is back in the box now. Come and see!"

"You know I can't. I couldn't even roll so
far. But seeing is believing."

"Then I'll bring the box," said the Apprentice;

'THE GREAT CAKE'

"So she did! Harry Cooper then? He had a big mouth like a frog's and stuffed his cheeks."

"Oh no! He would not swallow a raisin-pip. I left one or two in, and wished them to him. He took them out of his mouth with his finger."

"Then that little girl – Lily Long? She used to swallow pins as a baby and came to no harm."

"Oh no! She only ate the marzipan and sugar, and gave the inside to Molly Miller who sat by her."

"Then I give up. Who was it? [You seem to have been watching very carefully, or making it all up.]"

"Alfred Smithson, of course, Master," said the Apprentice.

"Go on!" laughed the old Cook. "I ought to have known you were having a game with me, and making it all up. Don't be ridiculous! Alfred Smithson is a plain hardworking man now, as he was a quiet sensible boy then. Cautious, you might say. Thought before he spoke. Looked all round before he jumped. He wouldn't let anything go down that might do him harm. Chewed before he swallowed, and still does, if you take my meaning."

"I do Master. Very well then. You must think as you like. But the star is back in the box now. Come and see."

"You know I can't. I couldn't even roll so far. But seeing is believing."

"Then I'll bring the box," said the Apprentice;

and he went and fetched it. He opened it under the old Cook's nose. "There this is the stuff, thank 'ee, in the corner."

The old Cook was sneezing and coughing, for some of the spices had gone up his nose; and when at last he had wiped his running eyes he looked in the box. "So it is," he said, "if my eyes are playing me tricks and tears watering."

"No tricks, baker, I put the stuff into a cake you made, and ate a cake of it. It might may go back into a cake, I think."

"Well, well!" said the old Cook into a knowing look, and then he laughed till he shook like a jelly. "So that was the way of it, as I never guessed. You were always a smart lad, and maybe you'll find some more adventures, or made 'em up I know not. But economical, that you always are. Wouldn't waste a currant, or a bee's knee of butter. So you nipped that little star out of the mixture while you were a-stirring it, and out of harm's way I guess you've kept it. Well that's cleared up. Maybe I'll have a go at naps now. But thank ye kindly for coming."

"Have ye now, baker!" said the Apprentice and wished him Good Day. But he turned back once before he set away. "A li'le same" he said, without any knocks "when you wake up, you might think again, if you have not gone too far in sleep."

'THE GREAT CAKE'

and he went and fetched it. He opened it under the old Cook's nose. "There is the star, Master. Down in the corner."

The old Cook was sneezing and coughing. For some of the spices had gone up his nose; but when he had wiped his running eyes he looked in the box. "So it is!" he said, "If my eyes are playing me tricks with this watering."

"No tricks, Master. I put the star there with my own hand, barely a week ago. It might go back into a cake, I think."

"Ah-ha!' said the old Cook with a knowing look, and then he laughed till he shook like a jelly. "So that was the way of it, and I never guessed. You were always a smart lad, though you had some queer notions, or made 'em up to tease me. But economical, that you always were. Wouldn't waste a currant, or a bees-knee of butter. So you nipped that little star out of the mixture while you were a-stirring it [and out of harm's way you've kept it]. Well that's cleared up. Maybe I'll have a quiet nap now. But thank you kindly for coming."

"Have your nap, Master," said the Apprentice and wished him good day. But he turned back now before he went away. "All the same" he said, without any Master, "when you wake up, you might think again, if you haven't grown too fat and sleepy."

But when he tried to walk nearer he [could?].
He never saw that Tree again, though he often
sought for it, and not long after he came to the
Lake of Tears in the middle of the Isle of the Wild
Wind
came [that time again], and [though release him?]
he found he was near the [Meadow?] of Faery [walls without?]
[to divert his own coming?].

Afterward [from a while] he tried to find the Tree
again, but he never saw it again. On [another?] [day?]
he came to the L. of Tears, where in the [midst?] [stood?] in
the Isle of the W.W., though he [distinct?] [knew] the ways
the lake lay [calm as still?] [calm as a]
lay unruffled as a mirror, as the island seemed
near. The [dark?] birches that grew upon it were
shining white, and were reflected in the lake [that]
lay calm and unruffled as a mirror. He took boat
and was [cruel as usual?], so he waded [and swam?]
out to the island; and for a long time it
seemed to draw no nearer, and then at last he
reached the shore he was [weary?]. He [sat down?] a
[great while?], and y^e [walked] in the forest he saw
but all the trees were [bare?], as in [full leaf?]
the [heavy branches?] in the [sunlight], yet there
was no [sound?] of [life?]. Suddenly he heard for
[?]

Lake of Tears
drafts and transcriptions

But when he tried to walk nearer the wood
He never saw that Tree again, though he ~~often~~
sought for it, and not long after he came to the
Lake of Tears in the middle was the Isle of the Wild
Wind
came about him again and when it released him
he found he was near the Marches of Faery walking toward[?]
~~the direc~~ his own country.

    Afterward for a while he tried to find the Tree
~~again~~ but he never saw it again. On one of his wanderings[?]
he came to the L. of Tears where in the midst of which was
the Isle of the W. W., though he did not know their names.
~~The~~ The Lake lay ~~calm and still~~ calm and even
lay unruffled as a mirror, and the island seemed
near: The ~~white~~ birches that grew upon it were
shining white, and were reflected in the lake which
lay calm and unruffled as a mirror. He tasted the water
and it was cool and sweet, so he waded and swam
out to the island: and For a long time it
seemed to draw no nearer, and when at last he
reached the shore he was weary. He found it was a
great island, ~~and~~ as he walked in the Forest he saw
that all the trees were fair/young and in ~~full leaf~~
their leaves trembled in the sunlight. Yet there was
no movement of air.   Suddenly he heard far
away

and the sun went dark.

Once he came to a lake which he had heard called the Lake of Tears, though he did not know why. He tasted the water and it was bitter, and his heart was saddened as he walked in the forest on the slopes above the lake, though all the trees there were young and fair and in full leaf, and the sun shone. Then he heard the Wind coming far away, roaring like a wild beast, and it broke into the forest, tearing up all that had no roots and driving before it all that could not withstand it. He put his arms about the stem of a white birch and clung to it, and the Wind wrestled fiercely with him, dragging away his arms; but the birch was bent down to the earth by the blast and enclosed him in its boughs.

At last the sun gleamed out again, and he saw all the leaves of the forest whirling like flying clouds in the sky, as the Wind bore them far away. Every tree was naked. Then all the trees wept, and tears flowed from their branches and twigs like a grey rain and some gathered in rivulets that ran down into the lake   lovingly

'Blessed be the birch!' he said, laying his hand upon its white bark. 'What can I do to show my thanks?' and he felt the answer of the tree pass through his hand and arm, and it said: 'Nothing' But if you see the King tell him. When he returns he will still the Wind and we shall But go away from here! The Wild Wind is hunting you. If you see the King tell him. Only he can still the Wind once it is aroused

LAKE OF TEARS

One day he came to ~~a lake which he had heard called~~ the Lake of Tears, though he did not know ~~why~~ its name. He tasted the water and it was bitter, and his heart was saddened as he walked in the forest ~~that~~ on the slopes above the lake, though all the trees there were young and fair and in full leaf, and the sun shone. Then he heard the Wind coming far away, roaring like a wild beast; and the sun went dark and ~~it~~ the Wind broke into the forest, tearing up all that had no roots and driving before it all that could not withstand it. He put his arms about the stem of a white birch and clung to it, and the Wind wrestled fiercely with him, dragging away his arms; but the birch was bent down to the earth by the blast and ~~its boughs~~ enclosed him in its boughs.

At last the sun gleamed out again, and he saw all the leaves of the forest whirling like ~~a flying~~ clouds in the sky, as flying before the Wind as it ~~bore them far~~ went away ~~but all the trees were naked.~~ Every tree was naked. Then all the trees wept, and tears flowed from their ~~branches and~~ twigs like a grey rain and some gathered in rivulets that ran down into the lake.

'Blessed be the birch!' he said, laying his hand lovingly upon its white bark. 'What can I do to show my thanks?' and he felt the answer of the tree pass ~~through~~ up his ~~hand and~~ arm, and it said: 'Nothing. ~~But if you see the King tell him. When he returns he will still the Wind and we shall~~ But go away from here! ~~I think~~ The Wild Wind is hunting you. If you see the King tell him. Only he can still the Wind once it is aroused

[script] Then he heard a sigh [script] Hears Wind [?] and can see no stars

◂◂ 177 ▸▸

Notes

Smith of Wootton Major

6 **Alf.**
Derived from Old English *ælf*, Old Norse *alfr*, and related to Modern English *elf*, *Alf* carries the meaning in all these languages of "elf", a supernatural (but not divine) being believed to influence human affairs. Elves were part of the folk-beliefs of Northern Europe, the "lower" rather than the "high" mythology of the gods. In Anglo-Saxon times the word was used in personal names as part of a compound such as Ælfwine ("Elf-friend"), Ælfbeorht ("Elf-bright"), Ælfred ("Elf-counsel"), names which come into Modern English as Alwyn/Elwin, Albert, and Alfred.

The earliest draft of *Smith* called the hero "*Alfred Smithson*". Strictly speaking, Smith's name would more appropriately have been Ælfwine, "Elf-friend", while Alfred, "Elf-counsel", would better fit the King, who counsels Smith to relinquish the star.

7 **"his tall white hat"**.
In a letter written to Roger Lancelyn Green in December 1967, Tolkien noted, "...Merton [his Oxford College] comes in [to the story]. Our present admirable little chef (with a v. tall hat) is, at least pictorially, the original of Alf" (*Letters*, p. 389).

10 **"It is fay"**.
Fay, "magic, possessing magical powers".

Afterword

68 **"On Fairy-Stories"**.
"On Fairy-Stories" was first presented in 1939 as the annual Andrew Lang Lecture at the University of St. Andrews in Scotland. The text was expanded for inclusion in the memorial volume *Essays Presented to Charles Williams*, a collection planned as a festschrift for Williams and published by C.S. Lewis after Williams's untimely death. Together with the short story *Leaf by*

Niggle "On Fairy-Stories" was published in 1964 as part of *Tree and Leaf*. The entire volume was then reprinted as a separate section in *The Tolkien Reader* in 1966. It is included in *The Monsters and the Critics and Other Essays*, edited by Christopher Tolkien and published in 1983.

Tolkien was deeply concerned to establish the true meaning of the term *fairy*. In a footnote to "On Fairy-Stories" (*Monsters and the Critics*, p. 111) he refers to *daoine sithe* (Old Irish), *tylwyth teg* (Welsh), and *huldu-fólk* (German). *Sidhe* is Irish, Scots Gaelic and Manx for a fairy mound, the dwelling-place of fairy folk, and by extension the Otherworld or Underworld. The equivalent Welsh term is *Annwfn*, often translated "underworld". Fairies themselves are called in Irish *daoine sidhe*, "people of the mound", and in Welsh *y tylwyth teg*, "the fair folk".

A strong belief in the presence in the human world of un-human beings with supernatural powers was to be found throughout the British and Irish countryside in the nineteenth and into the early parts of the twentieth century. Investigation of such beliefs and collection of the folk-stories, folk-sayings, and folk-customs (such as leaving a pan of milk on the doorstep before going to bed) that expressed them was the focus of the newly-developed discipline of folklore studies.

73 **Clyde Kilby.**
In 1964 Tolkien was contacted by Professor Clyde Kilby of Wheaton College in Illinois in the United States, and the two men corresponded after that from time to time. Wheaton was then in the process of establishing the manuscript collection and research facility devoted to the works of C.S. Lewis, J.R.R. Tolkien, Charles Williams, Owen Barfield, Dorothy L. Sayers, George MacDonald and G.K. Chesterton that became the Wade Center. In November of 1967, shortly after the publication of *Smith of Wootton Major*, Kilby asked Tolkien about the possibility of purchasing the *Smith* manuscripts. In response, Tolkien sent to Kilby in America a description of the draft copies and rough manuscripts, including his own recollection of how the story came to be. To Kilby's regret the College was not able to afford the price, and the manuscripts eventually went to the Tolkien Collection in the Department

NOTES

of Western Manuscripts of the Bodleian Library in Oxford.

74 **"The Great Cake"**.
The original title derived from the idea of the cake introduced at the end of Tolkien's abortive introduction to *The Golden Key*. The change in the final drafts to *Smith of Wootton Major* signalled Tolkien's change in focus from the cake to the boy; as well as a shift from allegory (where a pastry stands for a concept) to fairy tale (how an ordinary man ventures into fairyland and what he finds there). Less obviously, it contained reference to stories and authors external to the tale.

In a letter to his grandson Michael George, Tolkien wrote that the Smith title was "intended to suggest an early Woodhouse [Wodehouse] or story in the B[oy's] O[wn] P[aper]" (*Letters*, p. 370). Four early P.G. Wodehouse novels recount the comic misadventure of his hero Rupert Smith (he spells it "Psmith"), who begins as a schoolboy in *Psmith in the City* (1910) and matures into a quintessential Wodehouse hero over the course of *Psmith Journalist* (1915), *Leave it to Psmith* (1923), and *Mike and Psmith* (1935).

The Boy's Own Paper, whose readership is self-explanatory, was a weekly periodical of eight or ten pages. It was put out by the Religious Tract Society and had a remarkably long life, staying in continuous publication from 1879 to 1967. Issues featured science, natural history, puzzles, school and adventure stories, brief biographies of "Men who are Talked About" (such as Thomas Edison and Charles Darwin), as well as stories and serialized novels by popular authors like Jules Verne, Algernon Blackwood, Sir Arthur Conan Doyle and G. A. Henty.

Tolkien's title, a tongue-in-cheek homage to both these stalwarts of British fiction, was almost certainly not meant to be taken seriously in the context of the story.

74 **"Slidder than glass"**.
Slidder, an archaic adjective now obsolete, means "slippery; on which one readily slips". It comes from Old English *slidor* from *slidan*, "slide". The word's earliest recorded use is from the eighth or early ninth century in the Anglo-Saxon *Runic Poem* #29, *Is by oferceald unʒemetum slidor* ["Ice is excessively cold, immeasurably slippery"]. A

closer parallel to Tolkien's use of the word occurs in Robert Mannynge of Brunne's Middle English text *Handling Synne* ("Sins' Handbook") c. 1303, which describes a *brygge* [bridge] "as sledyr as any glas".

75 **"Version as Read Blackfriars".**
This event, sponsored jointly by the Prior of Blackfriars, Fr. Bede Bailey, and the Principal (not Master, as Tolkien incorrectly had it) of Pusey House, Fr. Hugh Maycock, was part of a series on "Faith and Literature".

Blackfriars is a Dominican Priory and Permanent Private Hall of the University of Oxford for the undergraduate and graduate study of Roman Catholic theology. It sits directly across Pusey Street from Pusey House, which was opened in 1884 as a memorial to Dr. Edward Pusey, a figurehead of the Oxford Movement. Pusey House, at the corner of Pusey Street and St. Giles', is committed to bringing the Church of England closer to the Roman Catholic Church and restoring to the Church of England its Catholic life and witness.

It is not surprising that the Prior of Blackfriars

and the Principal of Pusey House should have invited Tolkien, a Roman Catholic and a member of the Oxford University community, to give a talk as part of their series. It might have been surprising that Tolkien, so invited, presented instead a story of his own composition. His Introduction justified this substitution by noting that the story "contains elements that are relevant to the consideration of Poetry, with a capital P, or that some may find it so." There was Tolkienian precedent for such substitution. Invited in 1938 to give a talk on fairy-stories to an undergraduate society at Worcester College, Tolkien had instead read to the audience his then-unpublished short story *Farmer Giles of Ham*.

80 **"inappropriateness for 'modern children'".** Perhaps on the basis of the format (for the first edition was scarcely larger than the original Beatrix Potters published by F. Warne & Co.), Williams has misread the story's intent and intended audience. It is not for children, modern or otherwise, as Tolkien was at pains to make clear, writing to Roger Lancelyn Green that "the little tale was (of course) *not* intended for children! An old

man's book, already weighted with the presage of 'bereavement'" (*Letters*, pp. 388–9).

Genesis of the story

85 **G. MacDonald.**
George MacDonald (1824–1905), Victorian novelist and lay preacher, was the author of a number of fantasies for and about children, including *The Princess and the Goblin*, *The Princess and Curdie*, and *At the Back of the North Wind*, as well as two philosophical and spiritual fantasies for adults, *Lilith* and *Phantastes*. He also wrote a number of fairy tales, of which *The Golden Key* is perhaps the best known.

85 *The Golden Key* **as a "'fairy tale' for children".**
Nothing in the written correspondence between Tolkien and Pantheon Books suggests that the publisher intended the book for children. Michael di Capua's initial letter to Tolkien, dated 2 September 1964, simply invited him to write a preface to *The Golden Key*. Tolkien replied on 7 September, agreeing and inquiring about a deadline. Di Capua wrote again on 23 September 1964:

Do you agree that it would not be possible to address your preface to the young reader, even though this will be an illustrated edition of a story that MacDonald called "a fairy tale"? If you wanted to address yourself to this hypothetical child, I would be glad, but I suspect that trying to write about this story in that context might cramp you. I think you might find it most satisfactory to address yourself to an adult reader of MacDonald, and we can assume that any child who cannot cope with what you have to say will simply skip the preface. But again I leave the choice to you.

Since nothing in the preceding correspondence had addressed the question of young readers (indeed, had seemed to obviate the whole issue), it is possible that the subject could have been raised in an unrecorded telephone or face-to-face conversation to which di Capua's letter was a reply.

85   "collapse of the project".
In the end, *The Golden Key* was not published by Pantheon Books. In 1966 Michael di Capua

changed publishers, moving from Random House to Farrar, Strauss and Giroux and taking the MacDonald project with him. The book was published by Farrar in 1967, with illustrations by Maurice Sendak and an Afterword by W.H. Auden. The dust jacket featured a quote from Tolkien's essay "On Fairy-Stories" in which he said, "*the magical, the fairy-story . . . may be made a vehicle of Mystery. This at least is what George MacDonald attempted, achieving stories of power and beauty when he succeeded, as in* The Golden Key."

86 **"Jack's letter of October 9, 1954".**
"Jack" was Tolkien's friend and Oxford colleague C.S. Lewis, who died in November of 1963. The "recent collection" in which "Jack's" letter is cited is Lewis's *Letters to an American Lady*, edited by Clyde Kilby and published in 1967 by William B. Eerdmans Publishing Company. On 9 October 1954, Lewis had written to the "American lady", Mary Willis:

> Fairies – the people of the *Shidhe* (pronounced Shee) – are still believed in many parts of Ireland and greatly feared. I stayed at a lovely bungalow

in Co. Louth where the wood was said to be haunted by a ghost *and* by fairies. But it was the latter who kept the country people away. Which gives you the point of view – a ghost much *less* alarming than a fairy. A Donegal man told a parson I know that one night when he was walking home on the beach a woman came up out of the sea and 'her face was as pale as gold'. I have seen a leprechaun's shoe, given to a doctor by a grateful patient. It was the length, and hardly more than the breadth, of my forefinger, made of soft leather and slightly worn on the sole. But get out of your head any ideas of comic or delightful creatures. They are greatly dreaded, and called 'the good people' not because they *are* good, but in order to propitiate them. I have found no trace of anyone believing or ever having believed (in England or Ireland) in the *tiny* fairies of Shakespeare, which are a purely literary invention. Leprechauns are smaller than men, but most fairies are of human size, some larger. (*Lewis*, p. 32)

A curious corollary to Lewis's anecdote about the leprechaun's shoe is to be found in the Souvenir

Book of the 1992 Tolkien Centenary Conference. Here, Canon Norman Power gives an account of an evening with Tolkien at a meeting of the Worcester College Lovelace Club in 1938 (the meeting referred to above, where he read *Farmer Giles of Ham*). Canon Power wrote:

> As the long evening proceeded, the Loving Cup circulated, tongues were loosened, and we all became more relaxed and cheerful. The discussion debated the reality of Dragons and other denizens of Faerie. To my delight, Tolkien maintained with great learning and a wealth of literary evidence that there must be something real behind the worldwide awareness of what a dragon is. Questioned about other beings, Tolkien . . . emptied his pockets. A surprising collection of junk accumulated on the floor beside me, such as Bilbo or Gandalf himself might have been proud to possess. Mixed up with a large ball of string was a green shoe which Tolkien extricated. It was strange, about eleven inches long, and pointed, too large to be a doll's shoe. I touched this: it felt like the skin of some creature such as a snake or lizard. Tolkien maintained stoutly and

with apparent sincerity that it was the shoe of a Leprechaun (Centenary Book pp. 9–10).

Tolkien's draft introduction to The Golden Key

92–3 "edges of the canvas", "added frame to a picture".

Tolkien's images here strikingly recall the concept illustrated at the end of *Leaf by Niggle* when Niggle sees for the first time beyond the edges of his own canvas, the "remote and faintly glimpsed distances" and the hitherto unrevealed regions on either side, the country of which his Tree is a part. Tolkien argues much the same point in "On Fairy-Stories", where he faults the convention of dream narratives for enclosing "a good picture" within a "disfiguring frame". The mechanism of falling asleep and waking up is the disfiguring frame, for it negates the wonder of the dreamed content by its waking dismissal of the experience as "just" a dream. The idea is perhaps most extensively treated in the first part of *The Notion Club Papers* where the Club members discuss and criticize the appropriateness of various arbitrary "frame" devices by which

Time Scheme and Characters

97 The "Time Scheme and Characters" schedule exists in three states. The earliest consists of three manuscript pages of which the roughest is a year by year listing of events starting in 1000 with "Grandfather Cook born" and ending in 1120–21 with "Great Party Alf goes away and leaves Horner the M. Cook". Substantial marginal jottings narrate and expand the sequence of events. At the bottom of the page is a short list giving the ages of the members of Smith's family at the time of the story as follows:

   Smith 51
   Wife 51
   Nan 26
   Ned 28

The page is cancelled by a line drawn through from top to bottom. A second page, this un-cancelled, consists of narrative jottings chiefly concerned with the history of "Old Grandfather Cook" and his family. A third page extends this history to the village and its crafts. All three pages are continuous in the same handwriting and appear to be from the same time of composition.

A second, typewritten draft of the "Time Scheme" has corrections and emendations in ink, including a change from "Horner" to "Harper" as the name of the third Master Cook. The change retains the association with music, for Tolkien took care to make clear that this character, who plays no active part in the story, was to be a musician. A note specifies that *horner* is the appellation for "one who plays the horn", rather than, as with the rest of the crafts, one who works with horn as a medium like wood or stone. This change is retained in the third, fair typewritten copy, which is the one reproduced here.

Smith of Wootton Major essay

111 **"this short tale is not an 'allegory'"**.
Tolkien proclaimed his dislike of allegory so firmly and on so many occasions that one is tempted to see it as too much protest. In the

Foreword to the second edition of *The Lord of the Rings*, he wrote:

> I cordially dislike allegory in all its manifestations, and always have done so since I grew old and wary enough to detect its presence. I much prefer history, true or feigned, with its varied applicability to the thought and experience of readers. I think that many confuse 'applicability' with 'allegory'; but the one resides in the freedom of the reader, and the other in the purposed domination of the author.

In fact, as Tom Shippey has pointed out, Tolkien used allegory frequently and to good effect. He used it twice in his essay, "Beowulf: the Monsters and the Critics", once to portray the beginning of *Beowulf* scholarship as a fairy tale of the Sleeping Princess (the poem), in which all the fairies but Poesy are allowed to be present at the child's christening, and once in the allegory of the poem as a tower. What he seems to have disliked and repudiated was "moral" allegory (see his remarks on C.S. Lewis in his account to Clyde Kilby of the genesis of the story), in which the second level of meaning is related to a moral or ethical or religious or political position.

Nevertheless, he does concede that there is a level of allegory in *Smith* beyond the early idea of the very sweet cake, as he points out in his essay on the story. This is not the philological allegory proposed by Shippey, who sees Tolkien the scholar-fantasist as Smith, the skeptic Nokes as a critic-figure, and the Master Cook as a philologist-figure. Rather, Tolkien suggested the Hall as the village-church, the Cook as the Parson, and Cooking as personal religion and prayer. This level of meaning, however, is so recessive as to be almost invisible. Perhaps finally it is easier to accept Tolkien's preference for applicability "residing in the freedom of the reader" rather than allegory, "the purposed domination of the author".

115 **"O minutes great as years!"**
A misquotation or paraphrase of Keats's "Hyperion", l. 64: "O aching time! O moments big as years!" Thanks to Doug Anderson for pointing this out.

115 **Fairy > Faërie > Fayery > Faery.**

NOTES

Some etymology may be helpful in sorting out Tolkien's seemingly inconsistent and idiosyncratic spellings of this word. The modern word *fairy* comes from Middle English *faerie* from Old French *faerie/faierie*, "enchantment", from *fae*, "fairy", which in turn was developed from Latin *fāta*, "the Fates", plural of *fātum*, "Fate", the neuter past participle of *fāri*, "to speak". Thus Fate was "spoken; that which has been said", as for example a curse, or a blessing; and its derivation *fairy* had implications considerably darker than those the traditional phrase "fairy tale" carries today.

Tolkien clearly preferred the Middle English spelling and usage as well as the darker connotations. He felt that the word *fairy* as conventionally used in modern English had been debased, and divorced from its original complex and powerful meaning. He chose the older spellings to dissociate the word from its modern connotations of prettiness, delicacy, and diminutive stature, and return it to the older, considerably darker meanings it once had had. In Tolkien's lexicon the word properly meant "enchantment", especially by the spoken word, as in a spell or incantation.

In "On Fairy-Stories", he spelled the word *Faërie*. In some early drafts of *Smith* he used a modified Middle English spelling, "*Fayery*", close to that used by Chaucer in the Wyfe of Bath's Tale, where the Wyfe begins her story with the remark that,

> *"In th'olde dayes of the Kyng Arthour,*
> *Of which that Britons speken greet honour,*
> *Al was this land fulfild of Fayerye."*

Tolkien would have agreed with the Wyfe. In "On Fairy-Stories", he observed that "the good and evil story of Arthur's court is a 'fairy-story'".

His final spelling of the word in *Smith* simply dropped Chaucer's middle *y* and final *e* and simplified it to *Faery*. It is worth noticing that the word is consistently spelled "Fairy" when used by old Nokes, while the preferred spelling, "Faery", is standard usage for the story's narrator as well as for Smith, the Queen, and Alf.

117 **Nokes.**
Tolkien characterizes the name Nokes as "geographical" to distinguish it from the more typical

village craft names such as Smith or Miller. While etymologically it does indeed mean "living by the oak", it is also, as Tolkien knew, a type-name for a fool or ninny, an ignorant person. The name and the type have at least one other similar occurrence in his work in "Old Noakes of Bywater", who takes part in the expository conversation at *The Ivy Bush* in the opening chapter of *The Lord of the Rings*. This Noakes is deeply suspicious of Frodo's Brandybuck connections "away there in Buckland, where folks are so queer". That his doubts about the Brandybucks make it easy for him to believe ill of them is borne out by his lurid addition to the story about the death by water of Frodo's parents. "I heard she [Frodo's mother] pushed him [Frodo's father] in, and he pulled her after him". It is clear that for Noakes, whose judgement is called into question by his very name, no story of outlanders from across the river is too outrageous to be believed; in fact, the more colourful the better. Like many in Hobbiton (indeed just about everyone except Bilbo, Frodo, Sam, Merry and Pippin) Noakes is narrow-minded and xenophobic, automatically mistrustful of anyone not already known to him. Together with Ted Sandyman, Noakes represents the unimaginative, sceptical hobbit type whose opposite number is Sam Gamgee, with his romantic desire to see Elves. The name Nokes/Noakes thus functions as a kind of shorthand for wilful ignorance and prejudice.

121 **Wootton and Walton and the Wood.**
The village names in *Smith* are all etymologically associated with the idea of a wood or forest, which in the story is intentionally made to be their proximate location. Wootton Major is close to the edge of the Westwood. Wootton Minor, where Smith's Grandfather Rider comes from, is within its borders, a village in a clearing. Walton, where Smith's grandmother, Rose Sangster, comes from, is even deeper in the wood. Both the Woottons, Major and Minor, derive their first name from Old English *wudu-tun*, "TŪN [town] in or by a wood". The name Walton most probably comes from Old English *W(e)ald-tun*, "TŪN [town] in a wood or on a wold".

Tolkien may also have had a second meaning in mind for Walton, for the *wal* element could conceivably derive not from *w(eald)* but from *walh* or *wealh*, a Germanic word usually translated as "foreigner", applied by the Anglo-Saxon invaders to native speakers of Brittisc [British], a Celtic language. Over time the Germanic word and its derivatives became synonymous with British and Britons and eventually replaced those terms. Thus the name Walton might refer to a town [*tun*] of *Wealas*, speakers of what would then have been the British or *Wælisc* (modern Welsh) language. Four Waltons presently situated in the Birmingham region near where Tolkien grew up may be evidence of the presence of Welsh-speaking people there in the period after the Anglo-Saxon settlement; a circumstance of which he would certainly have been aware. The two meanings "wood" and "Welsh" are not mutually exclusive, however, and indeed may be related, in that Tolkien's location of Walton deep in a wood was intended to imply close proximity to and familiarity with his strongly Celtic-influenced Faery.

Celtic mythology, specifically Irish and Welsh, traditionally locates the Otherworld in the West, sometimes oversea or underground, but frequently in a wood. Tolkien's preference for a wood as the entrance into his Faery may owe something to his familiarity with "Pwyll", the First Branch of the Welsh *Mabinogion*. At the beginning of that story, Pwyll Prince of Dyfed, out hunting in a forest, encounters Arawn the King of Annwfn (the Welsh Otherworld) in a clearing in the wood. The two exchange shapes and Pwyll spends the following year in Annwfn, while Arawn rules over Dyfed.

The catalogue of Tolkien's personal library lists diplomatic editions of The White Book of Rhydderch and The Red Book of Hergest, two medieval manuscripts of the *Mabinogion*, from which he made his own transcription and partial translation of "Pwyll". Among his notes for "Pwyll" is a discussion of the etymology of "Annwfn".

128 **Sedgers, Crowthers.**

These are old words for story-tellers and fiddle-players. Since it is unlikely that modern readers would recognize either term, they seem used largely for their archaic effect. In fact, however, the verbal form of *sedger* was still in use in a corner of England in the early decades of the twentieth century, as Tolkien would have known. He contributed the Foreword to Walter E. Haigh's *A New Glossary of the Dialect of the Huddersfield District*, published in 1928, which lists s$\bar{e}$, past tense s*ed*, "to say, speak" from Middle English *seggen*; Old English secgan, "to say".

Tolkien had closer acquaintance with such old words through *A Middle English Vocabulary*, his lexicon appended to Kenneth Sisam's *Fourteenth Century Verse and Prose*. Here, much as in his essay, Tolkien glossed *seggers* (Middle English segge(n) "to tell") as "professional story-tellers", while explaining *crouders* as "fiddlers" (Middle English *croud, croup*, Welsh *crwth*, "fiddle"). His Middle English recension of *Sir Orfeo* included *crouders*; but when he translated that poem into modern English he changed *crouders* to *fiddlers*.

Since both are listed as musicians in his essay, however, *crowthers* must be different in some way from *fiddlers*. The instuments are comparable, though not exactly alike. *Fiddle* is self-explanatory and still in use, both as word and instrument, while the O.E.D. defines the now-obsolete word *crowd* as an equally obsolete Celtic instrument of the viol class, in early times having three strings but later six, four of which were played with a bow, two by plucking with the fingers. The distinction is partly etymological, *croud* being Celtic in origin, *fiddle* Germanic. Tolkien plainly wanted both.

The archaic words may have helped establish in his own mind a general sense of time and place. His essay, hardly more explicit than the story's "not very long ago nor very far away" opening, sets the scene in "an imaginary (but English) country-side before the advent of power-machinery". This gives a range of twelve or thirteen centuries, leaving the story afloat in time. The archaic words have the effect of anchoring it somewhere in or near the fourteenth century. Inclusion of the old words not in the tale itself but in the side-essay seems consistent with Tolkien's deletion of *slidder* from the Lake of Tears episode. The plain language of the narrative creates its own world, and focuses attention on theme, not period. The essay's introduction of the old words conveys remoteness, as of an isolated rustic setting, or of antiquity seen in historical perspective.

129 **Tolkien's views of Faërie.**
The nature of Faery as depicted in the story and

described in the accompanying essay contradicts in some respects Tolkien's earlier discussion in "On Fairy-Stories". There he wrote that, "if elves are true, and really exist independent of our tales about them, then this also is certainly true: elves are not primarily concerned with us, nor we with them. Our fates are sundered, and our paths seldom meet." In the story he shows what in the essay he states clearly, that the folk of Faery are "interested in Men (not necessarily primarily) and beneficently"; that the relationship is "one of love" and that inhabitants of Faery have "an ultimate kinship with Men, and have a permanent love for them in general".

133 **"OHMS"**

On His/Her Majesty's Service. An identifying stamp used by the government of Great Britain to designate official correspondence. As applied to the King it would mean that he was here a courier for the Queen, officially carrying her message to Smith.

143 **"The church has been 'reformed'. Memory survives of 'merrier' days".**

Tolkien's allegorical argument at this point, that the Hall (the Church) is no longer painted or decorated but has become merely utilitarian – "reformed" since "there are no longer songs, music, or dances" – may refer to the more extreme aspects of the Protestant Reformation. These discouraged decoration in churches, and severely reduced the performance of ritual and ceremony in religious practices and forms of worship. They also banned more secular celebrations and entertainments such as singing (except hymns) and dancing. His reference in the next sentence to memory of 'merrier' days recalls the expression "Merry England", a phrase evoking a utopian, pre-industrial way of life now ruined by the rise of commerce and the profit motive, a decline attributed to Wootton in the following paragraph in the essay. It may also be an allusion to a proverbial phrase often used to contrast the (presumably) worse present with a bygone but (also presumably) better therefore merrier time, such as Olivia's comment in *Twelfth Night* that "Twas never merry world since lowly feigning was call'd compliment:", or the Clown's observation in *Measure for Measure* that "Twas never merry world since, of two usuries, the merriest was put down, and the worser allowed by order of law a furred gown to keep him warm." The opening phrase, an aphoristic one-size-fits-all, was applicable to any situation, for example the Duke of Suffolk's comment on Cardinal Wolsey that: "It was never merry in England since we had Cardinals here!", or the more oblique, "It was a mery world (quod the papist) before the Bible came forth in englysh."

Hybrid Draft

158 The manuscript pages of this draft are apparently copied in part from four rougher-draft manuscript pages written in ink over now-illegible pencil. On these rougher pages, individual paragraphs are numbered in the margin from 1 to 7, but not in the sequence in which they appear on the pages. The numbering is clearly a scheme for the different and preferable re-ordering of the paragraphs as they appear in the handwritten fair copy.

161 **"his name (Starbrow) in Fairy"**.
The literal translation of *Gilthir* would not be

"Starbrow" but "Starface". The name is a word or word-compound deriving from Tolkien's invented languages. Proto-Eldarin GIL- is glossed in the Etymologies (HME vol. 5, *The Lost Road*, p. 358) as "shine", with the variant *gîl*, "star". Sindarin *thir* is harder to trace, but appears in the name *Caranthir*, "Dark face," the name of Feänor's fourth son. The etymology of *thir* is given in the linguistic journal *Vinyar Tengwar*, Number 41, July 2000, p. 10, as follows: *þîr* "face" (< *stūrē*). An earlier, slightly different derivation appears in the Etymologies under "THĒ -" look (see or seem). N *thîr* (*thērē) look, face, expression, countenance" (HME vol. 5, *The Lost Road*, p. 392).

161 **"at home he was called Alfred Smithson".**
Called simply "the boy" in the typed pages, the smith is consistently referred to as *Alfred* in the manuscript pages, while the character who in later drafts is called *Alf* is here called simply "the Apprentice". The name shifted its designate as the story developed, as shown by a singular instance in the typescript. On page three, for the only time, the first Cook bids farewell to "Edwy", with *Edwy* then crossed out and *Alf* written in

above. It seems clear that the decision to associate the Apprentice with Fairy by name must therefore have been made some time after the entire draft was written out. The name *Edwy* never appears again, and was obviously only briefly considered before being replaced. An Edwy (or Eadwig; the name means "happy war") was king of Wessex from 955 to 959, but since it is unlikely that Tolkien intended reference to Edwy of Wessex, he may have meant the name to be a variant of *Edwyn* or *Edwin* from Anglo-Saxon *Eadwine*, "bliss-friend" or "happiness-friend". This name, together with its variations *Edwin* and *Audoin*, figures significantly in Tolkien's two unfinished time-travel stories about the Fall of Númenor, *The Lost Road* and *The Notion Club Papers*.

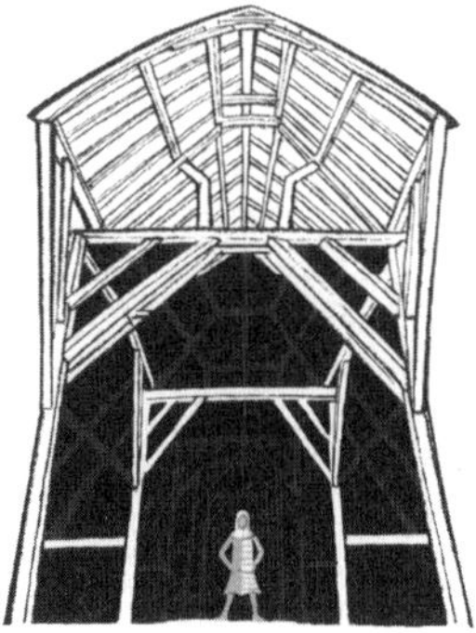

ALSO IN THIS SERIES

The Adventures of Tom Bombadil

'*Here is something that no devotee of the Hobbit epic can afford to miss, while awaiting a further instalment of the history of these fascinating people.*' So declared the jacket of this book when it was first published some fifty years ago.

One of the most intriguing characters in *The Lord of the Rings*, the amusing and enigmatic Tom Bombadil, also appears in verses said to have been written by Hobbits and preserved in the 'Red Book' with stories of Bilbo and Frodo Baggins and their friends. *The Adventures of Tom Bombadil* collects these and other poems, mainly concerned with legends and jests of the Shire at the end of the Third Age.

This special edition has been expanded to include earlier versions of some of Tolkien's poems, a fragment of a prose story with Tom Bombadil, and comprehensive notes by acclaimed Tolkien scholars Christina Scull and Wayne G. Hammond.

'*Professor Tolkien revealed in the verses scattered through* The Hobbit *that he had a talent for songs, riddling rhymes, and a kind of balladry. In* The Adventures of Tom Bombadil *the talent can be seen to be close to genius.*'—
THE LISTENER

ALSO IN THIS SERIES

Roverandom

While on holiday in 1925, four-year-old Michael Tolkien lost his beloved toy dog on the beach. To console him, his father, J.R.R. Tolkien, improvised a story about Rover, a real dog who is magically transformed into a toy, and his quest to find the wizard who can return him to normal.

The adventures of Rover, or 'Roverandom' as he becomes known, include encounters with an ancient sand-sorcerer and a terrible dragon, by the king of the sea and the man-in-the moon. Rich in wit and word-play, the story underwent a number of revisions and was originally considered for publication in January 1937, the same year as *The Hobbit*, but was abandoned when the publishers asked instead for a sequel, which culminated in *The Lord of the Rings*. *Roverandom* was finally published in 1998.

This edition is edited by Christina Scull and Wayne G. Hammond, whose introduction shows how the story is related to Tolkien's later works *The Hobbit*, *The Silmarillion*, and his *Letters from Father Christmas*. It includes all five illustrations by Tolkien himself.

'This is an old-fashioned story, yet it still speaks freshly today... would leap to life when read aloud to a child.' —
THE INDEPENDENT

ALSO IN THIS SERIES

Farmer Giles of Ham

Farmer Giles of Ham did not look like a hero. He was fat and read-bearded and enjoyed a slow, comfortable life. But after inadvertently scaring away a rather deaf and short-sighted giant, Farmer Giles' heroic reputation spread far and wide. Unfortunately for him, when the wily dragon Chrysophylax visited the kingdom, it was Farmer Giles who was called upon to do battle with it...

Like *The Hobbit* and *Roverandom*, *Farmer Giles of Ham* was invented by J.R.R. Tolkien at first to entertain his children, then grew and became more elaborate. Its final version is for readers of all ages who enjoy a good story told with wit and imagination.

This edition reprints the text first published in 1949, together with its original illustrations by Pauline Baynes which Tolkien thought to be a perfect accompaniment to his tale. Edited by Christina Scull and Wayne G. Hammond, it also includes the earliest written version of the story and Tolkien's notes for a sequel.

'A fabulous tale of the days when giants and dragons walked the kingdom.' — SUNDAY TIMES

ALSO IN THIS SERIES

The Hobbit

Bilbo Baggins is a hobbit who enjoys a comfortable, unambitious life, rarely travelling any further than his pantry or his cellar. But his contentment is disturbed when the wizard, Gandalf, and a company of dwarves arrive on his doorstep one day to whisk him away on an adventure. They have a plot to raid the treasure hoard guarded by Smaug the Magnificent, a large and very dangerous dragon. Bilbo is most reluctant to take part in this quest, but he surprises even himself by his resourcefulness and his skill as a burglar!

Written for J.R.R. Tolkien's own children, *The Hobbit* met with instant success when published in 1937. It has sold many millions of copies worldwide and has established itself as 'one of the most influential books of our generation' (*The Times*).

This pocket edition, published to mark the 75th anniversary of first publication, includes a foreword by Christopher Tolkien.

'A finely written saga of dwarves and elves, fearsome goblins and trolls ... an exciting epic of travel and magical adventure, all working up to a devastating climax.' — THE OBSERVER

and said good-bye, to the Apprentice; no one else was about. 'Good-bye for
now, Alf,' he said. 'I leave you to manage things as well as you can. I
hope things go well. If we meet again, I expect to hear all about it.
Tell them that I've gone on another holiday, a long one I hope; and that
when that's over I shan't be coming back'.

There was quite a stir in the village when the Apprentice gave this message to
people that came to the Cook-house. 'What a thing to do!' they said.
'And he's never made a Great Cake; it's still four years to the next. And
what are we to do without any Master Cook?' in all the arguments
and discussions nobody ever thought of making the young Apprentice
into the Cook. He had grown a bit taller, but still looked like a boy, and
he had only served for three years. In the end for lack of any better
they appointed a man of the village, who had a good name as a cook, in
a private way, though he was not much of a baker. He was a solid sort of
man with a wife and children, and careful of money. 'At any rate he won't
go off without notice' they said; ' and even a poor dinner is better than
none'.

Nokes, for that was his name, was very pleased with the turn
things had taken. For some time he used to put on the tall white hat
when he was alone in the kitchen and look at himself in a polished frying
pan (there were no mirrors in the village) and say; 'Good morning, Master!
That hat suits you properly, makes you look quite tall. I hope things
go well with you'.

They went well enough; for Nokes indeed a respectable Cook, and he had
the Apprentice. But in due course the time for the Great Party
began to draw near, and Nokes had to think about making the Cake. It
worried him a bit, for although with four years' practice he could turn out